BOOK OF BAYS

BOOKS BY WILLIAM BEEBE

TWO BIRD-LOVERS IN MEXICO	*Houghton Mifflin Co., 1905*
THE BIRD	*Henry Holt and Co., 1906*
THE LOG OF THE SUN	*Henry Holt and Co., 1906*
OUR SEARCH FOR A WILDERNESS	*Henry Holt and Co., 1910*
TROPICAL WILD LIFE	*New York Zoological Society, 1917*
JUNGLE PEACE	*Henry Holt and Co., 1918*
EDGE OF THE JUNGLE	*Henry Holt and Co., 1921*
A MONOGRAPH OF THE PHEASANTS	*H. F. Witherby and Co., 1918-1922*
GALÁPAGOS: WORLD'S END	*G. P. Putnam's Sons, 1924*
JUNGLE DAYS	*G. P. Putnam's Sons, 1925*
THE ARCTURUS ADVENTURE	*G. P. Putnam's Sons, 1926*
PHEASANTS: THEIR LIVES AND HOMES	*Doubleday, Page & Co., 1926*
PHEASANT JUNGLES	*G. P. Putnam's Sons, 1927*
BENEATH TROPIC SEAS	*G. P. Putnam's Sons, 1928*
NONSUCH: LAND OF WATER	*Harcourt, Brace and Co., 1932*
EXPLORING WITH BEEBE	*G. P. Putnam's Sons, 1932*
FIELD BOOK OF THE SHORE FISHES OF BERMUDA	*G. P. Putnam's Sons, 1933*
HALF MILE DOWN	*Harcourt, Brace and Co., 1934*
ZACA VENTURE	*Harcourt, Brace and Co., 1938*
BOOK OF BAYS	*Harcourt, Brace and Co., 1942*

WILLIAM BEEBE Book of Bays

HARCOURT, BRACE AND COMPANY, NEW YORK

TO
TEMPLETON CROCKER

ACKNOWLEDGMENTS

My thanks go to the Editors of The Atlantic Monthly, Harpers Magazine and the Bulletin of the New York Zoological Society for permission to reprint the chapters which appeared in their pages.

The photographs were taken by Toshio Asaeda, John Tee-Van and the author. Plates 14, 32 and 33 are the work of George Swanson.

PREFACE

THIS is a tale of unending curiosity; of unquenchable desire to know more of the lives—the homes, the food, the enemies, the mates—of certain wild creatures of sea and land. To satisfy this zoophily we interrupted unnamed beings at their meals five hundred fathoms down in the black Pacific, we interfered with hosts of others near shore from sea-elephants to eels, sea-snakes to baby sailfish. We exposed exciting lives by turning over heavy stones (and often, in compassion, heaved them back again). We clambered up cliffs to interview infant boobies, and slithered through the unreal world of mangroves after rare crabs, and held binoculars poised until our arms ached. The froth of the trip is in these chapters; the technical meat is served up in scientific courses elsewhere.

For five months on the slim, black yacht Zaca, we prowled along three thousand miles of Pacific coast from Mexico to Colombia.

Before we started on this expedition, the west coast of Central America meant to us only an irregular extent of meeting place of land and sea. Now we know it consists of forty or more bays, with extremes on the north of sheer desert, grading southward into typical tropical rain forest; vertically we envisage it from the tops of the coastal hills and mountains to what our nets brought up from a half-mile depth in the Pacific Ocean. Rarely we anchored off cities—Manzanillo, Acapulco, La Union, Corinto, Puntarenas—but in perspective these were

only occasional human intrusions into a region of wild beauty
which is seldom visited, and wholly unmarred by the activities
of mankind.

The closeness to the shore and the height of the Sierras—
joining the Rockies with the Andes—introduced an unexpected element of isolation, and made the series of bays and
their fringes of level land a chain of island-like areas, a linear
archipelago of sorts, with mountains and sea for boundaries.
So shut off from the rest of the mainland were many of the
bays that we hardly ever thought of any man-made limits;
Mexico, Nicaragua, Costa Rica, Panama—all were merged in
a long extended coast, a continental fringe of great interest.
Neither the scattering of kindly natives with whom we made
friends, nor land, shore or sea suggested republics or political
divisions.

In all this we reveled, comfortably yachted as to bed, food
and laboratory, and able to anchor close to the shore of tiny,
unexplored bays, with names rivaling those of the South Seas
in euphony: Banderas, Chamela, Tenicatita, Sihuatanejo, Rio
Dulce, Angeles, Guatulco, Santa Cruz, Tangola-Tangola, Fonseca (take a fresh breath!) Murcielago, Potrero Grande, Culebra, Braxilito, Piedra Blanca, Nicoya, Uvita, Golfito, Bahia
Honda, Chiriqui and so on. (Plate 1.)

For the second time Mr. Templeton Crocker had gener-
ously placed the yacht *Zaca* at the disposal of the New York
Zoological Society, resulting in the Thirty-eighth Expedition
of my Department of Tropical Research.

Our adventures and zoological studies in the eastern Pacific
on the *Zaca* in 1936, which crystallized into *Zaca Venture*,
reached from Cedros Island in the north to Cape San Lucas

and Mazatlan. The present expedition extended these explorations south to Panama and Gorgona Island, Colombia, limits which bound a very distinct faunal area.

As before, Mr. Crocker accompanied the expedition, and, as Patron Extraordinary, interested himself in every phase of our work in general, and in shooting desired specimens of birds and catching game-fish in particular. Perhaps the most valuable of all Mr. Crocker's qualities in promoting the success of our efforts was his willingness to limit or extend our stay in each bay, according to our estimate of its barrenness or its richness in scientific possibilities. If heavy surf or steep mountains forbade profitable investigation, we left, after an hour of exploration in the launch; if, on the other hand, a narrow entrance led into an expanse of sheltered beaches, sand alternating with rocky tide pools, and jungle creeping to the very shore, we settled down for perhaps a fortnight's visit. This enabled us to reduce collecting to a reasonable proportion of time, and afforded hours and days for observation of the living creatures themselves.

Mr. Crocker's friend, Mr. Maurice Willows, was with the Zaca as far as Puntarenas and made game fishing and insect collecting his special fields of endeavour. The physician of the expedition was Dr. Eric Liljencrantz of Stamford. There was, fortunately, no serious work for him on the Zaca, but again and again he was summoned by radio to cases of life and death on various tunaboats along our course. Toshio Asaeda again carried on his usual excellent and thorough work as photographer and preparateur.

Alfred Pedersen was again our Captain. Now that I realize that the Zaca was to be his last earthly cruise, I can only hope that if ever I ship for an expedition on any future voyage, whether on Acheron, Styx or Lethe, that he will be my helmsman. But on Earth he was the perfect Captain, so I fear me that while I vainly seek transport to the somber coasts of Dis, that "Stormy Pete" will be gaily tacking toward the Isles of the Blest.

The Zoological Society's scientific personnel was the same as on the 1936 expedition: William Beebe, Director; John Tee-Van, General Associate; Jocelyn Crane, Technical Associate, and George Swanson, Artist.

Our chief object was to study as thoroughly as possible the fish, crabs and mollusks, from tide pools down to five hundred fathoms, with more emphasis placed on ecological relationships, colours and habits than collecting. Constantly in mind, as a major problem of my own, was the accumulation of field data of use in evaluating the relationship of corresponding Atlantic and Pacific forms.

Political boundaries were, as I have said, practically non-existent to our conscious minds, but geographical configurations occasionally forcibly concerned us. Throughout the entire five months we enjoyed almost perfect weather, with two exceptions. There are two definite openings in the 2500-mile extent of the Sierra mountain ranges, one at the narrow neck of Tehuantepec, and the other where the great Lake of Nicaragua opens up a wide watery gap. The Northers of the Gulf of Mexico sweep across to the Pacific in sudden dangerous "Tehuantepeckers" for six months in the year, and farther south the corresponding storms raging across the great lake are known as "Papagayos." Except for these two intervals, the Pacific lived up to its name.

CONTENTS

CONTENTS

ILLUSTRATIONS

xv

ILLUSTRATIONS

xvi

ILLUSTRATIONS

ILLUSTRATIONS

xviii

BOOK OF BAYS

CHAPTER I

ELEPHANTS OF THE SEA

THAT you and I and our children should begin to reacquire functional tails is extremely improbable but not at all impossible. If these useful appendages were only distant arboreal memories, such a thing could not occur, but tails are very real things in our individual lives. They share with Faith in being "evidence of things not seen."

When we are three weeks old (referring to the tri-hebdomades of actual existence) we are the possessors of an amazing tail, in length about a fourth of our entire being, and in substance and musculature of greater importance than any of our budding, paddle-shaped limbs. It bears no resemblance to the slender objects trailed about by mice and monkeys, but is a tail comparable rather to that of a powerful shark. Our neck at the same instant shows four pairs of most excellent gill-clefts, aligned, clear-cut, unmistakable; transiently present throughout all the ages as if for possible prospect or eventuality.

Our tail does not degenerate in size as the weeks pass, but becomes gradually embedded in our body, and when we change our first shelter for an isolated life on the planet it has usually disappeared. I say usually because occasionally a child is born with a well-developed tail, twelve inches or more of skin, muscle and bone.

3

Most exciting and most personal is the fact that every one of us carries about four vertebrae or backbones which are useless except to remind us of the tails of yore—very yore. Attached to these bones are sometimes as many as twelve pairs of muscles, and with these the television of past ages has left the fish far behind and advanced to reflected life within olden jungles.

These muscles are irregularly distributed, and you—for all you know—may possess all the wagging or curling muscles well developed, while your closest friend must be content with only the depressors, and your great aunt goes through life unconsciously flaunting the elevators. Science, so far, is silent concerning the possibility of correlation of these three with characteristics of friendliness, timidity or spiritedness. A bad fall may make us painfully or dangerously aware of this inner tail, but aside from this, its vital interest is a reminder or a throwback to aquatic or arboreal ancestors.

I am endeavouring with considerable sincerity to escape from the subject of human tails, for I meant it as only an introduction to the consideration of sea-elephants, but having established my premise I am led by my pencil to one or two obvious but brief elaborations. Having redeveloped a tail how should we treat it? It is difficult to understand any feeling of shame in connection with our new appendage which would represent merely the nadir of our spinal column, with our head as the zenith. Only members of the Ku Klux Klan, occasional burglars and married women of certain benighted tribes endeavour to conceal their heads. If we search far enough back in our evolutionary closet we will discover skeletons of ancestors whose heads were little more than negative tails. Even

4

today there persists a little creature in the sands of our shores who is unbelievably close to the beginnings of fish, and consequently ourselves. Its name is Amphioxus, which significantly means sharp-ender, and it presents no evidence of swelled head as yet developed. Yet it can see, feel and swallow to its complete satisfaction. Even in our embryonic selves evidences are only too plain that our head and brain were originally fashioned from a string of vertebrae—say eight or ten. With too many of our fellow mortals the result of the toss of life—heads or tails—seems inconsequential; their cranium appears to fulfill the primary definition of Faith—"the substance of things hoped for."

The point toward which all this tail-talk is heading is the actual comparison of tail and gills. Like the brief period of totality of a solar eclipse when time itself seems halted for a moment, so for an appreciable duration of existence we seem to swim and breathe and have our minute being—an inchling shadow of ancient eons—submerged in the diminutive sea of a womb. Although tail and gills are both present at this moment, they differ radically in the possibility of persistence. Once a tail, always a tail. Our gills, however, momentarily bridging the years—say a matter of five hundred millenniums—even while we recognize them for what they are, begin to shift and bend and dissolve. We go to the trouble of developing four pairs of gills with skeletons and blood vessels ready to be nourished by a two-chambered fishy heart, all adumbrating a life beneath the water. Then swiftly, within the space of a few days we find the gills gone, transformed into a string of ear-bones, a lower jaw, larynx and tongue cartilages. In a fraction of time we have exchanged the possibility of breathing

5

water in the silences of the sea, for a throat and tongue muscles which will not only admit the life-giving air but enable us to play upon it as it passes, to fret it into audibility— to talk, pray, curse, sing, laugh, which no fish can do. It behooves us, occasionally, to stop, listen and consider the daily worth we extract from this swap in mid-evolution. Also thanks to the idiosyncrasy of a little gill, we can or must listen to the vocal efforts of our human associates. Finally, as a lifelong reminder of an auld lang syne, we retain one last gill throughout our life, the tube which extends from our ear into the throat. This is just to make good science out of the good poetry beginning:

> When you were a tadpole and I was a fish
> In the Paleozoic time.

Through the activity of certain hormones we might reacquire tails but we can never recapture the activity of gills; they are too evanescent and predestined. Which has brought me a step nearer to sea-elephants, which in turn stimulate thoughts of raccoons and whales.

The change from water breathing creatures into air breathing land animals is almost the greatest wonder of evolution of animal life on this whirling, lonely planet. That from a four-legged, scaly runner to a two-legged feathered flyer is less momentous; fish fly through the water in three dimensions, and besides, there are flyingfishes. But the marvel of marvels, utterly unexpected and inexplicable, is the deliberate regression from a fully adapted life on land back again to that in water.

Early on the morning of a November eighth I struggled

through the surf, and landed on a narrow beach of the island of Guadalupe off the west coast of Mexico. There before me was a herd, or more appropriately, a snoring of sea-elephants. They might all have been dead were it not for the snoring. Enormous grubs came to mind as an immediate simile. Then all thoughts of their shapelessness, their eternal sloth, passed and I saw them in sudden realization as Halfways, embodying all the drama and romance of evolution; I remembered those other Halfways in *Outward Bound*.

Only from occasional fossil skeletons can we imperfectly reconstruct the changes in past ages, but here in these Central American jungles we have links of living creatures which form a chain of as *ifs*, of remarkable continuity.

If we paddle along the inland creeks of the distant mainland we will be certain to see in the mud the five-toed tracks of raccoons. These familiar animals are excellent climbers and make their diurnal home in hollow trees, but they have a habit or a vice which is so pronounced that Linnaeus named them *lotor*—the washer. A coon may dig up a muddy bulb, or may capture a perfectly clean, shining beetle or a young bird. Soiled or not, every bit of food must be lugged to the nearest water's edge and thoroughly scrubbed before being eaten. In itself this has no special significance, but I like to think of it as a symbol of some creature of ages long past—a dainty dipping of fingers into the edge of a brook, which would end in complete submersion in the open sea.

A close cousin is the crab-eating raccoon which is built along more svelte lines, and possesses an uncontrollable passion for crabs in the live shell which draws it to water like a magnet, where it scoops up the crustaceans with its paws or

actually dives after them. When day comes, it scurries back
to land and the trees.

Unless it be a sloth, no animal would seem less a potential
explorer than an opossum. Throw an ordinary opossum into
the middle of a pond and after a few miserable squirms it will
probably drown. But do the same with a yapock or tropical
water opossum and it will dive and swim to shore with its
well-webbed hind feet, probably catching some aquatic creature on the way. As a marsupial and kin to kangaroos it is far
from the direct ancestral line of sea-elephants, but as an
aquatic backslider it is of vital interest. Only when its pouch
is filled with unweaned babies does it have to give up its
search for shrimps and fish.

Equally apart from direct lineage are three vegetarians of
these jungles which have deserted the traditions of their near
relatives and gone waterwards. The capybara is a giant guinea-
pig which seeks safety and food in the marshes and streams,
and the tapir, while calling horses and rhinoceroses cousins,
has shaken off the dust of their hooves and with wide-spread-
ing splay feet, goes squelching through the mud and swimming through the nights. Our third and last deviation is the
manatee or sea-cow. To find this being we must go across to
the Atlantic side of middle America, and to believe it when
seen, it must be touched. This is not very difficult, for when
found in a shallow ditch, it can be rolled up on the bank,
examined and returned, with no more opposition than would
be shown by an iron-hooped barrel of excellent rum. It were
better not to mention the face of the manatee, but if we
must we can only say that it has the largest harelip in existence, its nostrils are often mistaken for its eyes, and it would

resemble a sloth in expression had it any humour, or a pig had it any charm. Withal it has been given the name *Sirenia*. This unquestionably is due to its rounded head and its habit of holding its baby in its flipper while nursing it, which has led early myopic explorers to detect a resemblance to a mermaid or siren. It holds the extreme place in aquatic adaptations among shore or jungle animals, for its hands are flippers, its feet have disappeared and its tailflukes are useful only for swimming or for sitting upon.

Changes in habit, haunt, activity, structure are brought about more often than we realize by what might be called vacuums of opportunity. In our mid-American jungles we have plant-eating tapirs along the river banks, opossums diving after crayfish. But the more open water with its abundance of larger fish is an inviting no-man's land, to use the least apt phrase in the English language. And into this particular vacuum of opportunity otters evolved—developing into strong, swift swimmers and fishers. Crocodiles gave them healthful competition, but the field in general was theirs.

We may suppose that they increased and that young ones sought fresh fields, or rather salt waters, and found life possible and pleasant along the shore of the Pacific. As they spent more and more time in the water they developed thick, warm fur, shorter necks, with heavier bones for easier diving, and today we find the sea-otter one of the most interesting of all Halfways. Any hope of easy life in the open sea was probably rudely shattered by killer whales and sharks. So the sea-otters kept to the shallow water, where amid the kelp and offshore rocks they found ideal sanctuary. With unconscious wisdom they developed an insatiable craving for sea-urchins which no

9

other creature could masticate or stomach. So with haunts and food all their own, sea-otters prospered and remained sea-otters.

It is most fortunate that they have not been forced ashore again, for they have burned almost all their otterian land bridges behind them. When they haul out on a rock they can no longer walk but progress by awkward hops and springs, due to their over-developed hind limbs, with long, slender, backwardly directed, webbed toes. These great feet have but one desire and function, which is eternally to seize and push backward a webful of water. The front legs are small, and the hands are made for prying off urchins from the bottom, or crabs or shellfish. Then the otter swims to the surface, turns over, and devours its fistful of food. To crush the urchins the little hands smack them together. When a baby otter demands nourishment the same paws hold it conveniently.

Neighbors but not competitors of the sea-otters are herds of sea-lions, another animal link in aquatic advance, or terrestrial retreat, whichever way we care to consider it. We are now among a very vortex of characters which pulls both ways. Sea-lions have four real flippers—hands and feet become mittened paddles. Their ears are minute, their heads pointed, their very eyes flush—every inch is stream-lined and sinuous to a degree which induces death from despair in designers of submarines and planes. No fish is safe from them and yet they are held in thrall by the land. The young sea-lions must be born ashore and there suckled from two to five months. They still can raise their voice in loud vociferation although harmony has been lost in competition with the crash of breakers, and their efforts compare favourably with the acclaim of a peacock and the fanfare of a donkey. In spite of their dominant ocean life sea-lions can still walk, amble and gallop on dry land, although the latter gait is invariably towards the water, speed indicating prospective joy of submergence.

This node in our Pacific hegira brings us to the sea-elephants of Guadalupe which, by the way, judging by the size of their proboscises, deserve rather the name of sea-tapirs. To these we shall return when we have reached the end of the oceanic chain of life. The succeeding link is the little seal proper, whose hold upon the dry land of its forefathers is most tenuous. The young seal is born upon the shore, but sometimes even before birth it sheds its long-haired, porous coat and may be led by its mother into the water before the sun sets on the very day of its entrance into the world.

Although terrestrial ancestry is unquestionable both in the infant seal, whose primary need of land is less than a day, and any dolphin or whale, the psychological gap is significant and profound. Whether a four-foot pygmy dolphin or a hundred-foot blue whale, all have parted with their hind limbs and trust for progress to vertical sculling with the powerful tail. The hairs of these creatures are numbered and the number is exceedingly small. Never, by any chance, can they ever clamber ashore, or sun themselves on rock or sand. A Nazi, by some incredible form of self-hypnosis, endeavours to believe that the raising of the right hand indicates some cryptic proof of Aryan ancestry, but a whale, within the mittened web of his flipper, possesses indisputable proof of the five-fingered hand of his far distant, land forebear.

We lean on the rail and look out over the wonderful Pacific. A dolphin curves into view near at hand, expels a cloud

11

of air with a long-drawn sigh, and vanishes. Farther out, the fin of a shark moves slowly along but the creature itself does not break the surface. The course of evolution has run full circle—fish, amphibian, reptile, mammal; then the reverse, the actual links wholly unknown, but illustrated well enough by raccoon, otter, sea-otter, sea-lion, sea-elephant, seal, whale and dolphin.

Even the brief glimpse we had of the latter recalls our own developmental possibilities. The dolphin has redeveloped a swimming tail, although its rhythm is now vertically north and south, not east and west; but gills are gone forever. It need never touch dry land but it must ever rise, and rise again, to breathe air.

Whales are not Halfways. They have arrived at the last station in Waterworld and have used up their round-trip ticket. As for any future evolution, any turning again back to the land (a feat which the leatherback turtle has successfully achieved) there is no chance or possibility for whales: Man has seen to that. They can hope only barely to exist for a while longer: "That's all there is; there isn't any more."

And now let us return to Guadalupe, the home and the last stand of the sea-elephants of our northern hemisphere— the most fearless and tragic, the hugest, ugliest, sleepiest, and most helpless and hopeless links in all our chain of life.

On Templeton Crocker's yacht Zaca on the said eighth of November, we moved slowly through the calm waters of the Pacific about two hundred miles southwest of San Diego. A rounded bit of mist disturbed the horizon in mid-ocean. Although we had a comfortable mile and a half of water beneath our keel, the mist soon changed to the definite cloud which,

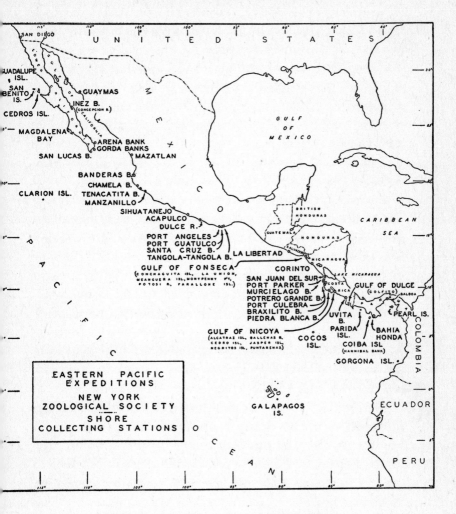

1. *Map of the Expedition.* From Guadalupe Island south to Bahia Honda and Gorgona we traversed 3000 miles of coast, and put in at every bay which promised scientific facts and specimens.

at a distance, is every island in the world except Barbuda—
which is nothing until you hit it.

The outline of the cloud hardened into a lofty ridge whose
barrenness was only partly softened by the thin mist along
the top. A little nearer and the human eye cut through the
cloudy grayness and distinguished colour—a great red and olive
cliff shot across with enormous seams of golden-yellow, while
here and there a petrified glacier of pale volcanic ash strove
forever to pour itself through unclimbable gullies.

It must have been a grand sight when this volcano first
broke through the ocean floor a mile and more below the
surface and sizzled and roared its way upward. The fish and
the squid which were boiled alive in the process were very
different from those swimming today about the Zaca, while
mankind was early in the making, still down on all fours, perhaps not yet free from scales. At any rate the crater nosed
itself above the surface and on up and up into the air until
it finally cooled off, a mile above the water. Whether storm-
driven Melanesians ever sighted it, or strange men drifting
down from cold northern regions, or if by some chance a
Toltec fisherman dared the trip from the mainland, one hundred and sixty miles to the east, we shall never know.

Back on the deck of the Zaca, as I approached closer, the
island became more and more barren to the eye. The time of
volcanic activity might well have been a dozen years ago instead of millions.

So sheer fell the cliffs that there seemed to be no beaches
whatever. Our engines slowed down and for minutes our fal-
lible eyes told us nothing more, so I resorted to high-power
glasses. As I focused, the blur cleared, distance dissolved. I

14

left the *Zaca* two miles behind and a vertical hillside crystallized into perfect detail. It seemed accessible only to creatures such as flies and geckos, yet within my field of vision was a score of quadrupeds, twenty-two creamy white goats dotted about at absurdly equal distances from one another. They did not move, they stood or grazed stiffly, and I could almost smell the paint, so much did they remind me of my old Noah's Ark animals. In this case, however, they were placed in such impossible situations that even a very small child would not have arranged them thus.

Not until our launch drew close to the breakers did the beaches become visible—narrow slopes of black lava sand. The first two were vacant. On the third I made out many elongate objects, rocks perhaps which had fallen from the steep overhead cliffs. But one of them bent upward and gazed at us, which is more than rocks can do, and we turned inshore and landed close to the first sea-elephants I had ever seen. (Plate 2.)

I walked up to the nearest great beast, an elongate mound of smooth fur, a half-grown male about ten feet over all. I sat down close in front of him and waited. He lay on his side apparently sound asleep, with small, helpless flippers dangling. His profile was like some weird cartoon or mask, impossibly and yet completely Hebraic, and he was having a nightmare. He snorted and snored and his muscles quivered as, in his dream, he twisted and turned to escape from some implacable killer whale. He heaved an asthmatic sigh like escaping steam, which vibrated throughout his entire eight hundred-odd pounds of flesh and blubber. His nose badly needed wiping and tears had formed large dark patches on the fur of his

15

cheeks. More tears now appeared. Carroll must have seen one of these lachrymose beings before he could have evolved the Mock Turtle.

Thus far, his breathing had been through the left nostril alone and now, in line with this conservation of energy, he opened a single eye, the right, and gazed at me. The orb was large, wistful, dim with tears and for a moment registered nothing. Then my sea-elephant perceived that something was amiss. It was not a killer whale which sat cross-legged so close to him, nor even a misshapen member of his own kind. His dull brain just registered an awful something.

He reared up on high, stretching up and up until his flippers hung in mid-air and he balanced on the posterior third of his body. Sphinx caterpillars draw themselves up into exactly this defense pose, but sphinx caterpillars do not open cavernous mouths lined with coral pink and expose four stubby white fangs; nor can any other creature in the world command the horrid jumble of sounds that emanated from his throat. It sounded like some noise-producing instrument which leaked at every rivet; snorts, double bellows, quivering snarls with hints of falsetto notes between. Then the beast curved himself into a crescent, elevating his tail end, spun around on the central axis and started for the water. He laboured along for perhaps twenty feet when he was overcome by languor, exhaustion or forgetfulness and collapsed into his former imitation of a fallen rock.

After a full minute, something of memory stirred in his brain and he again reared and looked back at me. To heave eight hundred pounds about on its pivot a second time was too much even to consider, so he simply bent back and back until his head almost touched his hind flippers, and gazed with uncomprehending wistfulness full into my face. Whether I appeared more attractive or less fearsome wrongway up, or whether—well, just whether—his head slowly sank down again on the sand. With a gargantuan sigh he cleaned out a deep hollow and erased me from his memory. Again my sea-elephant slept. (Plate 3.)

I glanced back along the beach whose smooth black sand was marked by a solitary great boulder at the water's edge. As I looked, this was rolled over by an incoming surge and I went toward it at once. It proved to be a gigantic male sea-elephant and this time death, not sleep, held it quiescent. It must have been dead several days but as it rolled back and forth I could see no sign of a wound. Its flippers waved dismally as it turned and the great proboscis flopped gruesomely about. When a wave left it stranded for a moment I stepped it off hastily and estimated its length as seventeen feet, which is not far from the maximum. Two young females and a male swam in as I watched, and almost touched its hide with their snouts before they turned and fled at high speed in the direction of the rookery.

At the south end of the bay near the water, in the partial shelter of a majestic promontory, was a closely packed mass of fifteen immature sea-elephants. Higher up was a gathering of twelve females and scattered about were fourteen others, six of which, including my first acquaintance, were males. Most of them awoke as we came near, moving their heads unsteadily and eternally yawning. The high-pitched snoring and roaring gargles almost obliterated the calls of gulls and the cheerful songs of rock wrens. But another sound soon

17

drew my attention. It was strangely like the beat of a tom-tom, now seeming to come from a great distance like the voodoo drums in Haitian mountains, and again resounding among the very rocks around us. It was mellow and vibrant. I climbed to the summit of the tumbled pile and in a pool beyond I discovered the source of the reverberations—a male quite as large as the one lying dead in the distance.

It was partly submerged, in the favorite crescent pose, with head and dilated trunk, and widespread hind flippers well out of water. The deep reiterated bellowing roars continued. At every utterance the proboscis rhythmically rose above and fell almost into the open mouth. Finally the beat died away with a few short, abrupt grunts like the finale of the nocturne of a howling monkey. For minutes the giant floated and watched me. Its hind flippers showed the elongated first and fifth toes which made the general webbed outline exactly like the half-moon tail of a swift-swimming fish.

Here, on this beach, were two and forty living sea-elephants. November was evidently the low tide of the year, between births, matings, and molts. Others would doubtless arrive in the course of the coming months, for a more seasonable census a few years ago listed many more.

I put out of mind that they were "sea-elephants" or "*Macrorhinus angustirostris*" or even "members of the order *Pinnipedia*." I tried to become aware of them more directly as creatures of their environment. I thought of them again as Halfways, and suddenly realized that they were rather Four-fifths. A small group of well-grown males returned from the sea, letting wave after wave lift them through the surf like sentient stranded logs. As they came slowly up the sand they appeared more than ever veritable creatures of the deep rather than transient immigrants to ancestral haunts. On shore, in all except bust measurement and comeliness, they fulfilled the definition of a mermaid—terrestrial forward, aquatic aft. The front flippers made fairly good crutches on which to rest, while the hind limbs dragged uselessly over the sand. Progress was by inchworming or humping along, and looking down from a high rock I seemed to be viewing a galaxy of mighty maggots speeding on their normal occasions. Nostrils could be closed to a slit camelwise, or opened wide and round as a dolphin's blowhole. But no mermaid or terrestrial being would hold each breath regularly for a half a minute between exhalations. I timed two sleeping animals and got sixteen, twenty-three and thirty-five seconds.

No sooner were the sea-elephants well up on the beach than they began to show slight but distinct symptoms of discomfort. Nostrils and eyes endeavoured to alleviate the heat, dryness or light by pouring forth a copious supply of mucus and tears. As I was passing one animal I received a shower of gravel in the face, which drew my attention to the fact that all those higher up on the beach had covered themselves with protective flipperfuls of sand.

Now and then some atavistic habit would obtrude itself unexpectedly through blubber-bound inhibitions, as when a half-dozing elephant lifted its fore flipper, bent back the terminal joints and with the projecting, rather well-shaped nails delicately scratched its cheek, or with the back of the same mittened hand gracefully wiped away a stream of tears. (Plate 4.)

As I watched these great beasts I thought of myself as I

19

was seven hundred and forty months ago—a being headed for a life on land, but fully equipped with gills, paddle limbs and tail. Could I have gone into reverse as had these sea-elephants, the gills would have dissolved into other structures, but the paddles and tail might have recouped their former usefulness. The Guadalupian giants, like myself, had passed, each of them, through a gilled stage but to no effect. Their paddles were grand paddles, hand made, but they had perforce to make shift in the water with lungs. Tails they had exchanged for sculling feet, while dolphins, their aquatic superiors, had discarded feet for consummate flukes. So are we all enmeshed in the glorious pattern woven of earthly evolution.

Sea-elephants are indeed caught in the maelstrom of Halfways. Their present home, for which they are dominantly moulded, and the squids and fish which form all their food, are beneath the surface. Yet each female must struggle ashore to give birth to her offspring, which suckles or sleeps or just lies six weeks or more on land. Mating takes place soon after the birth of the pup, and eleven months later the succeeding generation appears. Another necessary haul-out occurs at molting time when whole plaques of skin and hair peel off and are shed together.

Where the elephants go when they leave no one knows. Two things of which I am convinced are that they are more nocturnal than is usually thought, and that their speed in the water and power of deep descent are very great. On shore, sleeping sickness seems to be their chronic manifestation of abounding health; in competition for the least common denominator of activity they challenge sloths and turtles and win easily. But this phase of their life is deceiving. When the mighty webbed feet are widespread and held tightly sole to sole, they form a sculling apparatus second only to the flukes of a dolphin. Twice, as we went from shore to ship I saw shadowy forms passing with incredible swiftness beneath the launch, and I am certain they were not sharks, but sea-elephants.

The general size, shape and appearance of the females and young males are seal-like, but the huge masters of harems are three times as large as their mates, reaching, it is said, twenty feet in length and a maximum weight of perhaps four tons. They have developed a thick, tough breastplate of rough hide, a cuirass of corrugated leather which protects them in their jealous battles with rivals. The contests are seldom fatal and consist chiefly of much roaring and rearing, and hurling of themselves at each other, striking downward with their short canines. The objectives are the tender proboscis and the eyes, and I saw two half-grown welterweight amateurs each of whom had lost an eye in precocious encounters. When cornered, even the young males would rush at us for a few feet, but the sortie would invariably end in a doze of exhaustion. With sea-elephants on land the dream is mightier than the reality.

Let us leave the somnolent herd for a while and glance up and along the thousands of feet of steep cliffs. All Guadalupe seemed barren and dry and only along the very summit was there a line of ancient trees, pines and oaks of species reported to be found only on this isolated crest. Three decades ago Edward Palmer, the botanist, visited the island and found it a paradise of birds and plants. One out of every four of the latter was peculiar to the island, while the Guadalupe caracaras, juncos, finches, flickers, petrels, towhees, rock and house wrens were also found nowhere else in the world.

In the course of years, cats, rats and mice escaped ashore from ships, and finally someone with more faith than brains turned loose a few goats. The pelts of the latter proved valueless and their numbers are now estimated at sixty to eighty thousand. Every growing thing, green or brown, leaf, sprout, seed, root or bark within reach of these acrobatic capricorns has vanished. The trees on the summit are fighting desperately in spite of shredded bark, and their lessened foliage still gleans moisture from the swirling clouds and vitalizes a few small springs. But every cone or acorn which falls to the ground is instantly devoured by mouse or goat, and the end of all plants and water cannot be far away.

The cats have blotted out one species of bird after another until only the rock wrens, as far as I could see, were left in any abundance. Some trick of nest building must have baffled the felines. Curiously enough, the mice are reported as very common, the cats evidently preferring birds at present, with eyes on the rodents for a future change of diet.

I clambered for some distance up two canyons, dry arroyos without a single living sprig, and came across two carcasses of cats and three half-eaten goats. When about a hundred feet above the water I saw at one side a patch of bright green grass and other more succulent growths. I got as near as I could, following a well-worn goat trail. At the end, by standing on tip-toe, I could just reach a few leaves. I examined the weedy refuge and saw that even a goat could not climb up nor leap down within nibbling distance. Thousands of little hooves had stamped where I stood, the face of the rock in front was worn smooth with the search for foothold, while safe in the overhung cranny the botanical tantalus flourished. In their fight for life, goats have been observed drinking salt water and at low tide feeding eagerly on exposed beds of kelp. This is the terrible struggle for existence which has been brought about by the casual impulse of one unknown man.

I saw nothing of the mice, but at the south tip of the island while I was crawling over a pile of rocks, I surprised a cat feeding on a large crab. She was a horrid creature, yellow and gray fur all awry, eyes gleaming. She snarled silently at me and fled slinking along the shadows, finally to vanish into an inaccessible crevice. The something of paradise which Edward Palmer saw has evolved into something of a hell. Only the rock wrens seemed wholly happy. They hopped and ran over the sleeping mounds of sea-elephants, snapping up a fly now and then and giving thanks in explosive bursts of song.

The two score of sleepers or near-sleepers scattered about the beach seemed to have never a worry in the world. Throughout thousands of past generations their half-and-half lives must have found natural enemies few in number. During their evolution sea-elephants seemed hardly to have had healthful competition. Newborn pups, to be sure, had to be careful lest three or four tons of father land unexpectedly and fatally upon them, and the battling males must have won their fights and yet kept muzzles and eyes from harm. Occasional serried marks of teeth have been found on the hide of sea-elephants showing that sharks are not wholly negligible dangers, and killer whales are an ever-haunting fear, if not in nightmares on shore then at least amid the waste of waters far out at sea.

When I was watching a pair of wrens well up on the beach, a few falling bits of rock attracted my attention and I saw a diminutive landslide emanating from the hooves of a scrambling goat. On the shore we had seen evidences of recent rock slips of serious extent. A single earthquake might loose an avalanche which could conceivably wipe out the whole herd of sea-elephants.

In ages past as various land animals worked their way seaward, a most important adaptation was the counteracting of the cold of prolonged submersion. This was easy to accomplish and a dense, thick undercoat of fur in otters and fur-seals, or the development of blubber in sea-elephants and cetaceans, answered every requirement. In these north Pacific waters all was well with the world until the arrival of a race of tissue-skinned, hairless beings. They could not really swim, but had to move about in floating affairs more or less at the mercy of the winds. If sea-elephants could talk they could have applied this description equally to jellyfish and human beings. The shivering newcomers began to wrap themselves in thick fur coats and to light and warm themselves with blubber oil, and the end of an era came clearly into view.

Seals have been seals for at least fifty million years, but the slaughter hereabouts began only a short hundred and forty years ago. Today the Guadalupe fur-seal has almost gone, for the last observer who visited this island saw only three at the entrance of a cave. Two hundred thousand fur-seals were slaughtered on Guadalupe. On one beach which I visited, the stones were as smooth as if a glacier had worked upon them, but in reality they had been polished by the eternal passing and repassing of eons of generations of seal flippers. Doubtless the legions of slain seals helped to protect our grandmothers from chilblains, but today nothing remains of the Guadalupe fur-seal but a few fragments of old skulls in museums and perhaps an ancient, moth-eaten cloak in some forgotten attic chest.

All the northern sea-elephants left alive on the planet Earth are the pitiful handful which seeks sanctuary on these narrow beaches. It was a terrible thought that, were we the kind of human beings who worked havoc here in the past, we could have slain every one of the trusting, stupid creatures around and over which we stepped. Fortunately the Mexican government has been persuaded to pass a law protecting this forlorn hope, and it seems as if the creatures were, for a time, holding their own. In the southern hemisphere the related species has been afforded protection in time, and is thriving.

The unexpected onslaught of mankind, the steel spear heads, the powder and shot all seem so manifestly unfair; the ghastly rapid invention of murderous tools appears so anticlimactic to the slow, thorough march of evolution through all the ages.

I looked about at the helpless elephants of the sea and became aware of them in a new light. Platinum and radium and certain Old Masters are not necessarily of supreme beauty, but rarity enshrines them in a false glamour of sorts. And so in the light of tragedy, the phocine pogrom of the past, the voice and the figure of these native Guadalupians assumed a dignity and a charm, as a peacock's scream is softened by distance, and mitigation of a grotesque figure comes with approaching dusk. I felt a certain responsibility and concern as a member of the race of men who had brought them to this critical pass.

I would have liked to have them understand my horror and. regret.

Such sentimental emotions were not lessened by the apparent pathos of wistful, limpid eyes and streaming tears, but at this point my scientific acumen intervened and banished bathos. So I turned my mind to other matters.

CHAPTER II

LIONS OF THE OCEAN

ANY well-considered, conventional account of the beginning of a scientific expedition should always commence with the statement that the beautiful yacht lay quietly alongside her wharf, when suddenly the throb of life awoke within and spread along her keel, whereupon she headed seaward, her bow rose to the first lift of Old Ocean, and so on! But when, on only the third day out, such a phenomenon as sea-elephants materializes, all preceding and contemporary events and experiences dwindle and evaporate from memory.

However, to eliminate any initial break in the Zaca's log, I will record that at five o'clock in the morning of the sixth of November, 1937, the yacht did leave her above-mentioned San Diego dock. Five hundred and eighty-five mornings before, she had pushed off from the self-same moorings on our first trip, and, as now, had passed apparently identical battleships, and in the outer reaches, unchanged pelicans, cormorants and gulls.

Soon after settling down to a steady offshore speed we sighted a most remarkable object, as much like a great, black, tossing coffin as anything. Drifting alongside, we found it to be a wrecked, derelict airplane target. From its voluminous folds we garnered a harvest of crabs and other sea-folk who had accepted it as an ultra-modern sanctuary, just as their

27

ancestors had found refuge on the wrecks of Phoenician galleys.

In early afternoon we anchored off the forlorn hamlet of Ensenada to get our Mexican clearance papers. This hamlet had begun existence as an unsuccessful gambling hell, and now showed signs of resuscitation as a Mecca for American quail hunters and game fishermen.

After dark we stopped and submerged our first electric night light. This initial experience on each expedition invariably reminds me of nights spent in light-houses, when hosts of migrating birds hurtle toward the magnetic beacon. The results of a sub-surface light at sea are always as unpredictable as they are mysterious, in addition to being of considerable scientific importance. Later, I shall have more to say about them.

This first night, as the Zaca's impetus slowly gave way to drifting inertia, I saw that deep-sea lanternfish had risen to the surface. Every five or ten feet one of them appeared, quietly floating. All had come from appreciable depths, perhaps a quarter mile or more, drawn by some inexplicable psychological impulse up from eternal darkness to the temporary surface blackness of night.

As I had observed in the case of the bathysphere searchlight, our present bright illumination had little or no effect upon these abyssal fish, and they drifted along in total disregard of the electric beams. Writ in gleaming hieroglyphics on their bodies was their own particular cartouche in symbols and numbers of cold fire. Just as a battleship at night can flash its name in blinking code, so each species can be recognized by its refulgent patterns. All which I scooped up this evening were California lanternfish (*Myctophum californiense*). Their escutcheon of identity was a luminous right-angled triangle, together with a horizontal line of portholes, broken into seven and ten.

Even before we drew in the surface light, the wind began whistling through the rigging, and when we swung about and headed for a distant, invisible speck in mid-ocean, the elements took complete charge and for twenty-four hours we rolled and writhed in half a gale and a cross swell which reduced sleep and meals to ineffectual parodies. The only pleasant memory is of the Zaca being trailed by a quartet of albatrosses, soaring steadily, progressing effortlessly, each a perfect, living gyroscope amid the howling wind and the smother of shattered waves.

Then came calm and the wonder of Guadalupe and its elephants. We came, we saw and we finally left on the evening of the ninth, headed for our old anchorage at Cedros. The following day, at noon, we sighted the little group of San Benito islands, and what we saw from the deck of the Zaca persuaded us to anchor off the largest.

With almost never a human eye to see and appreciate, this part of the Pacific offers exhibit after exhibit of supreme zoological interest, combining circus, arena and scientific satisfaction. We were still almost breathless with the wonder of our sea-elephant experience the day before, yet here, only one hundred and sixty miles to the east of Guadalupe, on these tiny islets, a second, new adventure awaited us, equally interesting and definitely more exciting.

In strong contrast with the steep picturesqueness of Guadalupe the San Benitos were low and flattish, and instead of helpless, lolling sea-elephants, static upon the beach, these islets were alive with herds of virile sea-lions.

As soon as the Zaca anchored and a boat could be launched we started for the nearest island. The foreshore and upper terraces seemed to be pitted with great numbers of small, dark objects. As we came nearer and began to rise and fall on the breakers, the brown things not only increased in size but began to move, and come closer to the water. When we were about fifty yards from shore, several hundred sea-lions rushed down the beach, plunged in and swam at and past us, paying little attention to us or to the boat until they were between us and the open ocean. I feared at first that in their headlong spurt we might be upset, and I jumped overboard into three feet of water to try to steady the small dory. This only resulted in my being almost knocked down as three youngsters banged inadvertently against me. I was only glad it was not one of the half-ton males. The roars and splashings were beyond description, and when an oncoming swell raised the water to neck depth, I could see a host of dark forms shooting about beneath me. On the top of a wave we drove the boat high and dry ashore, and carried cameras and glasses up to the terraces. (Plate 5.)

The first, most noticeable thing was the all-pervading scent of ammonia, and secondly, the difficulty of keeping our footing, for the rocky beach and sloping uplands were worn smooth as glass by the centuries of attrition of thousands upon thousands of bodies being dragged along. Every lion was gone from our vicinity, but now and then we came across family parties of two to five, piled athwart one another, sound asleep. We walked around and photographed them while they

2. Guadalupe Island. This is the last sanctuary of northern sea-elephants.

continued to snore, and their muscles twitched in exciting leonine dreams of the sea. The moment that one of them opened an eye, pandemonium broke loose, and at the sight of us terrible invading bipeds every creature fled at top speed for the water.

On the lower part of one beach I found two large animals lying quietly, and yet watching us. I thought they must be injured and unable to move, but when I approached and touched them they languidly lifted their heads and I saw that they were half-grown sea-elephants. The distinction from the other San Benito inhabitants was not due to accident or paralysis but psychology. Persistent prodding aroused them into a few protesting writhes and wriggles, but almost at once they closed their eyes again, sighed deeply and we became to them only the unreal figments of a dream. I was glad to know that these animals had begun to spread out from Guadalupe, and hoped it meant the beginning of a new colony.

As I have said, the sea-lions showed great fear of us as long as they were on land, but once in their more familiar element, every emotion was subordinated to that of curiosity, and they turned and crowded back close to the outer edge of the surf, every eye glued on us. I watched the great green breakers rise, curve and crash, and silhouetted in the translucent hollow of each I could see dozens of water-baby sea-lions, rolling over in the tumbling surge, then turning and letting the backwash rush them out again.

The mob of chocolate-brown heads of the old ones projecting from the clear emerald water, the blue sky overhead, the ash-colored and red ridges around us, and the black, out-iutting rocks made a strikingly colourful picture.

31

3. *Bull Sea-elephant and His Harem of Females.*
With little emotion they watch our approach.

Creeping up from one side and carefully peering through a natural arch or crevice in the lava ridges, I looked out upon a fresh, undisturbed beach. The entire upper half was solid with dark brown or pale yellow, mummy-like forms lying every which way. Among and over them ran turnstones and rock wrens fly-catching, while gulls and ravens screamed and croaked as they flew overhead. As we looked and listened we were struck with the startling difference in voice between the two kinds of cetaceans. The pair of sea-elephants which we had just interviewed had given vent only to unpleasant rumbling, raucous gargles. But the sea-lions filled the San Benito air with loud, sharp, staccato barks or Arks! higher in the females and deep and resonant in the big males. These barks had a peculiarly human timbre, and frequently we called out in answer, thinking that some distant member of our party had shouted.

In their island sanctuary the sea-elephants had simply crawled up a gravelly beach and lain quietly. But here we were constantly impressed with the way the herds had affected the whole appearance of the islands. For a half mile or more inland the generations of sea-lions had acted as organic glaciers and ground and worn down and polished the hardest and sharpest volcanic outcroppings.

I sat on an isolated ledge at the head of a small beach and counted eight small, matted and trampled brown pelts of baby lions which had come to untimely ends. As I watched the deserted beach, to my surprise a young sea-lion scrambled out of the white smother of waves and began hitching itself up toward me. For a moment I hoped that its apparent tameness indicated a third sea-elephant and the first baby I had seen. My glasses showed it to be a sea-lion and extremely thin. The upper parts of its little limbs and its ribs showed clearly through the skin. Before it had reached the first of the exposed rocks it had fallen over five times, and now and then it stopped, swallowed and gave a silent cough. I sat immovable and at last it reached a red boulder at my feet, slippery and worn mirror-smooth. It spent many minutes trying to climb up the low ridge where I was seated, a feat which any well sea-lion could have accomplished in a single effort. But this pitiful little chap would only roll over backward and then have a paroxysm of coughing. At last it gave up the attempt and crept under the shelter of an overhanging ledge, and there sat in the sunlight turning its head from side to side. When it saw me approach it opened its eyes and half turned, but had no will to do more. I watched it for a while, so rare a sight is a sick wild animal. I then sent it a little prayer for a speedy end to its pain, and left it.

Our last sight of a live sea-lion came this same night when the *Zaca* was still anchored a mile off shore. Our surface light was put out and attracted hundreds of six-inch silversides. The current was then cut off for a few minutes and when again turned on, a small sea-lion was curled about it. He immediately snapped up several fish, drove the remainder away for good, and vanished into the blackness of the watery night.

At the beginning of the above paragraph I advisedly used the word *live*, for I am compelled to add to my account a shameful epilogue. After the expedition had come to an end and we were back in New York, the shocking news reached us that, for a consideration, the Mexican powers that be had rescinded their protection over the sea-lions of the San

Benitos. This news was later confirmed, and recently taken photographs show only too vividly the present aspect of the islands. Apparently every individual sea-lion has been slaughtered and its flesh cut off to make canned meat for dogs. The hides and skeletons cover the beaches and uplands. The pall which now fills the air is the stench of decaying carcasses; in place of the clear, sharp *Arks!* there is only the buzzing of flies; some extra pesos line the pockets of a few Mexicans, and the escutcheon of man's trusteeship of wild life on this planet has received another bar sinister.

It may be that a remnant of the animals escaped, and, with the unconquerable faith in life and existence, with which we like to endow the splendid vitality of wild creatures, a forlorn hope of Benito sea-lions may again creep fearfully out upon land, and try to reinstate themselves, to bring forth their babies, and to enjoy life, freedom and the pursuit of happiness as they know it.

CHAPTER III

A DAY OF ACCIDENTS

FOUR hours after leaving the San Benitos we were dredging on our old station east of Cedros Island. The only changes were the increased cold of the water and bottom mud, and the startling increase in number of Japanese diving for abalone shells near the sleepy Indian village described so vividly by Francis Preciado three hundred and ninety-seven years ago.[1]

On to the south we continued, along the full length of Baja California, around Cabo Falso, and past the never-to-be-forgotten, great granite masses of the Gray Friars. The tiny factory in San Lucas Bay, the anchored tunaboats, the sloping rock carpeted with cormorants and sea-lions, the pelicans, vultures and caracaras—all were waiting for our return, as they had watched us leave two years before. This time our stay was measured by hours, so I went with helmet and hose straight to the mysterious garden of eels—my third visit.[2]

First I had tried to net them, then I used traps, and finally a double charge of dynamite caps, fired as I crept toward them in my helmet. All to no effect. Now I intended to see what a whole stick of dynamite would do. I slipped down the ladder on the first dive of this expedition, and the first fish I

[1] Zaca Venture, page 6.
[2] Zaca Venture, pages 60 and 190.

35

saw I took as a good omen for the whole trip; a thirty-inch golden grouper, which, with two plebeianly hued fellows, swam slowly past. I went on through clouds of black-and-yellow, purple-and-green wrasse, and a few steps brought me to the edge of the eel colony. There were a hundred or more, projecting six to eight inches out of their holes, bodies bent against the current—all waiting for me. They drew down slowly out of sight as I fixed my charge directly over their tunnels and returned to the surface. Immediately upon the explosion I descended again, I scraped and dug, I used up all my oxygen in vain efforts. Not a sign of eels, alive or dead! Hundreds of small fish drifted upside-down in all directions, but to a depth of at least two feet there were no eels. I gave up defeated.

A postscript to this effort has reached me in a letter from Mr. Vernon Brock of the Oregon Fish Commission. It relates to a visit he paid to this exact spot two years after this last attempt of mine, and I quote direct:

I want to thank you very much for your letter and directions for finding the eel garden at Cabo San Lucas. We found the spot without any trouble, and I am certain that it was the exact spot from the photograph that you sent; however, we found not the slightest trace of the eels. . . . Last September there was a very violent storm at Cabo San Lucas which destroyed much of the village and I feel it quite likely that the storm destroyed the eel garden also.

And so came the second tragedy following our trail on this expedition; the first born of man's cupidity, the second elemental. The last sight we had of this village at the end of the continent, was of the Mexican and Indian women walking slowly home from the factory, the children playing on the shore, and the men leaning against the nearest upright thing, waiting for Time to pass. When the hurricane was over, we were told that all but three of the flimsy habitations were washed out to sea, and many of the people were drowned. That the raging tide and sea shifted the garden of eels I can easily believe; that it destroyed the creatures themselves I seriously doubt. I feel that these eels are immortal: upon them is no spot of vulnerability!

From Cabo San Lucas to Banderas Bay is some three hundred miles, and southeast, if the compass needle swings true. For us it was an afternoon, a day, and a morning. The day, which was also the fourteenth of November, was one of those when one thing happens after another. The night before, I lay in my bunk, thinking of things just past; of the ever-spreading effects of my dynamite, the sudden manna provided for fish and octopus. Or of the peso, which on impulse, I had given to a tiny, grimy scrap of a Mexican child at Cape Lucas. He had clutched this enormous wealth close to his one garment and fled at top speed. Once I saw him fall flat, to rise with eyes and mouth full of sand, but both hands clasping the largesse. The gift, I fear, could hardly have brought him adequate recompense, for to attempt to spend such a coin in such a place would be to create a parallel to the million-pound banknote. The chances were even, that a father or an uncle would claim it, with the result that the usual leaning posture would be altered to a tequila-induced horizontal one.

The future, as when I woke the next morning, the future pouring into the funnel of the present, was always a clear stream, and as I came on deck early on the fourteenth, the cur-

tain went up on the beginning of the first small adventure
of the day. Far astern I saw a speck in the sky. It might have
been a very distant booby, or a bee close at hand, but a second glance showed a labouring land-bird, and before it settled
wearily on deck it resolved into a small, brown, rather long-
tailed sparrow, claiming Zaca sanctuary after an eighty-mile
flight from San Lucas. It fed and drank and we caught and
identified it—a little clay-coloured sparrow, first cousin to our
eastern chipping. It may have bred as far north as Great Slave
Lake in northern Canada, and it is known to winter as far
south as the tip of Lower California so many weary, watery
miles away.

Towards noon the helmsman drew my attention to a strange
bird wavering along close to the water. Except that we were
one hundred miles from San Lucas I should at once have
said "Owl!" It came nearer and circled the Zaca, and now I
exclaimed with astonished conviction "OWL!" With nothing
for size comparison, I should have added "Barred," although
this species does not live within many hundreds of miles of
this part of the world.

The owl headed back as if to retrace its long journey to the
nearest land, but its owlish heart sank at the prospect and
again it turned and this time came straight for the yacht. At
last it alighted and we secured it, a pale buffy burrowing owl.
It was the western form and its home was on the distant
peninsula of Lower California. Wherever it was hatched it
was resident and in this part of its range it never migrated,
merely taking short flights from one part of its natal plain to
another. So this excursion far out to sea was purely accidental,
and its rounded wings and the softness of its plumage must

38

have made the more than thirty leagues of watery expanse a major flight in its life, and a most grievous hazard for this small waif. One inexplicable factor was the calmness of the sea during the past twenty-four hours. Any violent storm or strong wind was eliminated, and yet here was the owl one hundred miles off shore, very tired but far from being completely exhausted. It snapped its beak bravely and gazed at us with its great yellow eyes, apparently as amazed as were we to meet under such conditions.

Long discussions and still longer ponderings on the reason for this sea-going owl led only to another unanimous "Don't know why." The context in memory of a "beautiful pea-green boat" seemed as reasonable as anything.

Soon after this, another living being flew on board, also a creature of the night, clad in soft browns and patterned with subdued, nocturnal hues, and whose flight was as silent as that of the owl. This was a large moth, stretching full six inches from tip to tip, and appropriately named *Erebus odora*.

This lovely moth seems to have a predilection for the sea and for ships, for I have recorded it more than a dozen times as flying far off shore at night in various regions of this hemisphere. This one, however, must have flown all night, coming out of the East; the watery darkness making its route a veritable Erebus—a terrible "valley of the shadow of death."

It alighted near me on the yacht, on a tangle of dark-brown rope, and without shift of position came to rest upside-down, disappearing, although under the brilliant shadows of the awning, as by the wave of a magician's rod. The great moth had flown with rapid, zigzag flight toward the spot which was the Zaca. Yachts and coils of rope must certainly have been

39

beyond its experience in the jungle, yet without hesitation it chose the best background and attitude for more complete obliteration than it could have achieved anywhere else within my realm of vision on deck.

I gently raised its fore wings and it took no fright; perhaps it was tired, perhaps the intuitive workings of instinct whispered that immobility was the best negation of edibility. It was very beautiful; dark chocolate brown with double, veiled ocelli of scales on the hind wings, and wavy lines of lilac, gray, buff, black and a great emerald question-mark on the fore wings. In detail it was exquisite and delicate, in general it was a cryptic knot on a piece of old rope. It must have left shore in the darkness, so it had flown all the hours of daylight. Again we checked the consensus of our human minds: "We don't know!"

After lunch a young brown booby flew overhead. This time we had to deal with one of the most abundant seabirds of the region, which aroused no surprise at being encountered two hundred miles from its nesting grounds toward which we were headed. We needed it for information as to its feather parasites and its food, so we shot it. It was a bird of the year, so it had no family for which it might have been fishing. Its food was for its own sustenance alone, and it had done what no airplane could do. It had taken on board an extra load of six California flyingfish, some of which were fully eight inches long, and which aggregated sixty per cent of the whole weight of the bird. A bombing or a passenger plane can lift and carry not more than thirty-three per cent of its weight.

In the afternoon I was called to the stern where a dolphin, changeable as a fire opal, was being drawn in, hand over hand, on the end of the trawling line. As it came slowly toward the motionless screw of the *Zaca*, another dolphin rushed swiftly across the wake, hesitated a moment and passed on. Only this is not as clear as it sounds, the confusion resulting from our impoverished English language. The first dolphin was a fish— *Coryphaena*—related to jacks and bonitos. The second dolphin was the *Delphinus* of myth and story, a true mammal, a small whale of sorts which loves to leap and sport at the bows of ships. I have never seen the latter attack a hooked fish and the present instance was no exception.

It occurs to me that by applying the method of priority to common names, as is done with scientific terminology, clarity may sometimes ensue. In the present case Linnaeus gave the names *Coryphaena* and *Delphinus* respectively to the fish and to the mammal; unrelated creatures which today, in English, we confuse under the common name of Dolphin. I find that the first use of this term in literature was in the fourteenth century, where the word was written *Delfyus* and *Dolfin*. So for my own satisfaction and I hope of others, I shall hereafter call the fish *Dolfin*, and the mammal *Dolphin*—thereby alleviating at least optical if not oral or aural confusion. (These four final words introduce another sensuous chaos which I pass on for remedy to some better linguist than I.)

The food of our first dolfin also recalled myth and poetry for it had swallowed a good-sized paper nautilus, owner and all, the fragile, paper-tissue shell quite unbroken, although it had run the gauntlet of scores of teeth in jaws and pharynx.

Shortly after this we entered an extensive slick. For miles even small ripples were ironed out by some thin, oily, surface film, such as often persists after masses of floating seaweed

have decayed and sunk from view. Flocks of northern phalaropes found good feeding here, and lingered until the Zaca's
bow was almost among them before taking flight.

Some day I should like to write the entire life history of a
phalarope. To do this, with any adequate realism, would en-
tail actually being one of these birds. Physically they are sandpipers, yet in psychology and environment they are as far
apart as if they were penguins or gulls. The mental shift, although radical, is not unique in the realm of birds, namely,
the assumption of courtship on the part of the females, together with concomitant advantage of size and brilliancy of
colour. In the flocks of phalaropes we encountered there was a
very evident persistence of pairs, hinting of a permanence
throughout life due perhaps to petticoat dominance.

The additional ability to swim and to live for protracted
intervals at sea, with a facility hardly less efficient than any
gull or duck, is really an unexpected and quite inexplicable at-
tribute of a virtual sandpiper.

From bill tip to tail the phalarope is blood-brother to willets, yellowlegs and snipe. The texture of the plumage seems
the same, in length of leg and general facies there appears no
real difference. Only along the edges of the toes do we find
slight extensions of skin, lobate like the webs of the common
coot. This and this alone is the only external evidence that,
instead of spending the winter running along the rims of
tropical sloughs and shores, these birds live and feed hundreds
of miles out at sea. At times of severe storms they seek the
safety of the nearest land, but only temporarily. Slim toes
betoken littoral life; lobed toes, months on the high seas.

The paddles of the phalarope are for a lifetime—but what

of shorter periods? When deep snows cover our northern hills, we humans strap on snowshoes or skis, and plod, run or leap over the soft whiteness. But the ruffed grouse has been doing the same thing, and far better, ever since its identical ancestors picked their way over Pleistocene snows, a full million years ago. To avoid repetition, even after a quarter century, let me quote a few lines from *The Bird*, which I wrote thirty-five years ago in the Zoological Park while watching a captive grouse. "The ruffed drummer of our woods walks about in summer on slender toes over moss and logs, but when soft, deep snows come, his weight would make it difficult to keep from being buried at each step. So Nature provides him with snowshoes. From each side of each toe a broad, horny, comb-like fringe grows out; not a web of skin which might soon freeze, but rows of horny projections, like a myriad extra claws. This distributes his weight so that he trots over snow through which a fox sinks deep and flounders awkwardly at every step."

When the snow melts we kick off our skis, and when from under the blanket of forest drifts, the first arbutus and wintergreen appear, the horny fringes drop off and on slim, dainty toes the grouse mounts his favorite log and sends out the first ruffle from his feathery drums.

The phalarope, however, must scamper about the Arctic tundra, fashion his simple nest and brood his eggs (using the pronoun avowedly) with his paddle blades still unloosed.

Such small things keep vivid our interest in evolution, especially as we may be sure that there are other correlated characters of which we are still wholly ignorant. We have the answer, the final result before us, but we know nothing of

43

the inception, the development and the way of success in this new field of sandpiper life.

As I lay flat in the pulpit in the bow of the yacht, observing the birds bobbing daintily about, feeding and watching our approach, I saw, as almost always, the little wakes of the gyrating, darting skaters of the sea, *Halobates*, marine cousins of the insect water-striders of our ponds. After dark, and putting a fitting end to all the small events of the day, a sea-snake was captured in a net and aquariumed for observation in the morning.

As I looked back upon the day at sea, I counted nine creatures captured or observed, two insects, one fish, one snake, four birds, and one mammal. They had come at odd times, in different ways, none was of great rarity, and they seemed quite unconnected. Then suddenly I saw them as a whole, bound together by their relationship to the land, and everyone, and the characteristics of everyone assumed a new interest.

The fish dolfin—the *Coryphaena*—was set quite apart as having nothing whatever to do with the shore or land. He was one hundred per cent marine. But the other eight all had some connection with the land, either direct or at least ancestral. The sparrow, the owl and the moth were all accidental, what we might call fifty per cent air and fifty per cent land. Twelve or fifteen hours must have been the utmost during which they had fluttered perilously over the alien element, and the Zaca was definitely their only alternative to immiment death.

The phalaropes, to be sure, were at sea by their own volition; they had left the solid earth and the shore and trusted

44

themselves to the bosom of Old Ocean, certain of finding an abundance of food, and safety from the enemies which ever threaten their more terrestrial relatives. But this sea change was a transitory and a tenuous one. When a gale lashed the surface into great waves, these birds fled to land, and at the end of winter the call of an Arctic home brooked no denial. Here, for the first time in our list, we perceive an anatomical acknowledgment of winters at sea—the tell-tale lobes along the toes.

The sea has a much stronger claim upon the booby, although we must grant the same demand on the part of the air. This bird is tied to dry earth by mate, nest, eggs and young as surely as the phalarope, but its food throughout the entire year is harvested on the high seas. While it has the broadest kind of webs on its feet, excelling in extent even such swimmers as ducks and gulls, yet it seldom alights on the water. Its skillful fishing is controlled by gravity and the air, simulating a feathered arrow or winged harpoon in accuracy and in swiftness of entering and leaving the water. If I had to apportion the life of the booby among the three "elements" I should say land thirty, sea thirty, and air forty per cent. Far more than its natatorial equipment is its wonderful aerial adaptation of long, narrow, powerfully-muscled wings, and the streamlining from beak to tail. It must be seldom that the hungry waves ever claim a booby victim.

As unlike these birds in relationship, appearance and mode of life as can be imagined, are the sea-snakes. These metaphrastic sea-serpents exact nothing from the air except oxygen for breath. In spite of everything which has been written on the subject, I firmly believe that they are completely divorced from the land of their ancestors, forebears from the stem of the cobras, and that the young snakes are born and live from birth at sea. Our water snakes and moccasins show little or no adaptation to aquatic life. Their submersions are too infrequent and sporadic. These vipers of the sea have most efficiently flattened, paddle tails, and musculature seems also to have been affected, for on rocks and sand, these reptiles are capable of only feeble progress. Like the coral snakes of the land, these advertise their venomousness with a Joseph's coat of brilliant yellow and red and black scales. Pitiful remnant of all the mighty reptiles of old, ichthyosaurs, plesiosaurs, mosasaurs, which swam and dominated the seven seas, there remains today only a score of sea-snakes and still fewer species of sea turtles.

The intricacy of a problem, which is at once the joy and the despair of the naturalist, is manifest when we try to provide *Halobates* with a place in our ennead category. At first thought I am tempted to class it together with the sea-snake in having broken away, in comparatively recent times, from its fellows of the land. Then I remember that, to use an Irishism, its relations which live on land, live on the water. For this brave little water-strider, in former incarnations strode, as do its relatives today, upon the calm surface of our fresh-water ponds and streams. How it has changed its drink (if indeed it *does* imbibe), or its foothold on the denser surface film of salt water, or what it does when the sea is torn into shreds of spume, we have still to learn. I do know however, that instead of attaching its eggs prosaically to the leaves of water plants in ponds it deposits thousands of orange spheres, poetically

46

and effectively, to the vanes of floating feathers, pinions dropped by gull or booby, phalarope or albatross.

We finally come to a member of our own warm-blooded mammalian class, whose adaptation to ocean life is perhaps the most wonderful of all. With mementos of ancient piscine relationship still clinging to flesh and bone, the dolphin, as we saw in our sea-elephant theme, has experienced in its ancestry all the joys and pains of leaving the sea and attaining full quadrupedal, lung-breathing life in the open air on land. Then, quitting all this, it has returned to its original home, hampered now by having to mitten its fingers, lose its hind limbs, develop a propelling tail and yet still depend on air for the breath of life.

Thus ends our brief of life and death on sea and land of nine casual visitors to the *Zaca*. My tale seems but a record of ignorance, a smattering of half-truths, in comparison with what might be told. But the idea in the abstract is a fascinating one, and if it arouses our curiosity and enhances our desire to know more, it is worth while.

CHAPTER IV

A LADDER OF LIMPETS

BANDERAS BAY is so large that in small maps of Mexico it is usually the only bay given a name throughout the entire western coast, south to Panama. Its very size and open character made it one of the least interesting of the forty-odd we were to visit. When the high mountains first came into view in early morning, I examined the chart spread out on the deck-house, and suddenly one of my earliest geography lessons came vividly to mind. I had been asked what Cape on the North American continent was the most mumble-mumble? And I answered "Cape Corrientes." It was the correct answer but I was reprimanded and made to repeat the word, because I gave it an inexcusable rolling of the rr's, in imitation of what I had heard was the Spanish pronunciation. I now raised my head, looked at the great promontory, and shouted "Cabo Corrrrrrrrientes!" exactly as I had a half century before. I waited, but this time there was no reprimand, although there ensued sarcastically solicitous questions as to my sanity.

After traversing the great bay we drew slowly up to our anchorage, which was any place where our chart and constant lead heaving showed to be over twelve fathoms, and a mile or more from the shore. Customs were quick, because they consisted only of a bow, a salutation, a drink, a cigar and a signature. Here, as in many other places to come, there was no trouble, no suspicion, but an insatiable curiosity on the part of the customs officer to see a real yacht from topsail to toilet.

Leaving the captain to do the honors we all went ashore. This latter is the correct word, for the small Mexican town of Penas boasts no wharf. I should hazard a guess that all imports to Penas from the sea must be waterproof, or of a higher specific gravity than saline H_2O. The surf was rather high, but when we leaped out at the psychological moment with cameras and nets held on high, we were only overshoe.

The country and surrounding mountains showed the usual semi-arid type which characterizes so much of western Mexico. We walked through street after street and up the tiny rio to the south side. There we crossed the stream on the most spindling and shaky of swing bridges. It dangled in mid-air yards above the marshy trickle, doubtless measured to extreme flood season when the omnipresent debris of dead tree-trunks must have hurtled down from the highlands. The birds set the key to the country; grackles and silver-beak tanagers in the town, perching hawks watching fearlessly, filled with curiosity, while black and turkey vultures scrutinized us hopefully for signs of early demise. There were, besides, large blue kingfishers, kiskadees, small green macaws in threes, and finally a pair of glorious scarlets.

Quickly as we had come ashore, walked out into the country and returned, underground gossip channels had caught up with us, and a small urchin would shyly approach and offer an unfortunate lizard, usually tailless, or a still more ruined butterfly. Most of the houses were rather tumble-down, patched with gasoline tins and bits of rusty corrugated iron,

49

but frequently through half-open doors we caught glimpses of splashes of brilliantly coloured flowers in rear patios. Now and then a house was sandwiched in, which actually had a painted façade and bright gingham curtains in the windows. From these leaned forth attractive painted wenches who passed the time of day with us as we sauntered by. Even here the strange tale of our interests had penetrated and one scarlet-cheeked girl, with the mongoloid cheek bones and slant eyes of an Indian, vanished, and when she reappeared held out to me a shell. I recognized it as one for which we had searched in Guadalupe and found only one. I drew forth money to pay for it but she waved it aside with a smile and said: "*Nada dinero; es solamente un juguete para un niño.*" She persistently refused, so the "*Niño*" accepted his "toy" with gratitude, and made his best Spanish manners. It would be embarrassing to have to give to this desirable orange-hearted turban shell a specific locality label.

We passed old, old Indians gossiping on the corners, men making fish nets, one really lovely elderly woman sitting at the entrance of her house with unselfconscious tears streaming down her cheeks as she seemed to be mumbling prayers. Now and then unbelievably tiny, naked infants, on seeing us, walked, crept or ran with all the force of their chubby legs to escape from our path. Some were patently terrified, but none wept.

We went to the old, half-finished, half-ruined cathedral which was begun many years ago, and in 1929 the people had somehow scraped together fifty thousand pesos to complete it. Then the revolution came and the soldiers took it all. Now the blind windows are stopped with sacking and the great, curved, rose-to-be-window at the back of the altar is blocked by a thin film of thatch. Tanagers and sparrows are nesting in the altar framework, yet the bell rings the hours and calls to Mass. A sign warns all females to cover their heads and dress with modesty before entering.

A few yards beyond the church we were astonished to see an ancient automobile, of ripe vintage but newly painted. There were four men on their backs underneath it, attempting either to assemble or to fasten it together. The story was that it had been carried thither on the backs of numberless peons and deposited here, although in Penas the passable stretches of navigable roads could be measured by yards. Standing around were cowboys garbed as for some Hollywood rodeo, with elaborate saddles on the tiniest of horses, enormous revolvers and often two exceedingly heavy belts of cartridges, bright sashes and top-heavy sombreros of more-than-oriental splendour, together with spurs of a size fairly to puncture the diminutive *caballos*. On their faces were amused grins, and I am sure that among their soft phrases must have been the Mexican equivalent of "Get a horse!"

A small boy volunteered information which completed the evolution of transportation. He said that beyond the little stream, out of sight, was a landing field to which an airplane came now and then from Guadalajara. Here were peon, horse, car and plane, and the most useful of all was the peon.

We returned along the sea-front where there was a promenade of sorts, consisting of a rough walk, with benches rapidly reverting to their original elements. Here, at the sign of Manzanillo Cerveza, six musicians played the wildest, most fascinating of rumbas, and girls in spangles danced on the tables,

51

as being more smooth than the surrounding stone floor. From the shore, unending lines of burros clambered up, laden with panniers of great, rounded beach stones which, with inadequate mortar, were meant for the walls of new houses. I was sitting on the doorstep of the single-roomed custom house when I felt a soft, moist nose nuzzling under my arm. Twisting around I found a half grown peccary begging for a piece of the dulce which I was eating. I scratched its side and the little creature immediately rolled over on its back, grunting with ecstatic joy.

We had "done" Penas. There was nothing wildly exciting or unexpected about it all, and it was one of the most impoverished little places I ever visited. Yet our memory of it was almost perfect, of a charm of utterly unspoiled simplicity. Again and again it seemed as if the tableau in every street had been carefully arranged for a Hollywood set. As for being stared at, or annoyed by undue attention, we might have been invisible. And yet to many of the inhabitants we must have seemed as strange and amusing as actors in circus or cinema.

As we started for our boat, the sun sank exactly at the southern tip of the bay, and I shouted aloud "¡Adios, Cabo Corrrrrientes!" much to the amusement of a dozen Penasians within hearing. Only the custom house official, now in mufti shirt and trousers, shorn of all the regalia of officialdom, rushed after me to salvage his pet peccary, which had evidently lost his heart to me and my dulce, and was preparing to follow me through sand and water into the boat.

The second day in Banderas Bay may be summed up in two words—oysters and boobies. To collecting and studying the fauna which interested us the shores of the bay were hostile. Our tender human bodies, our stature of only six feet were foiled by the dense thorn scrub, and the steep shores which defied our seines; rocks tore our dredges and the absence of intimate coves and land-locked baylets allowed the swells and breakers of the open Pacific full sway.

Rumors of the wonderful oysters which grew off the north shore were reiterated, and their size and flavour increased with each repetition, so the *Zaca* was headed toward the Ideal of all oyster beds. We picked up a Mexican marooned in a dugout, towed him for a while, then he dived and brought up a small, poor-looking mollusk. I went down in the helmet in only twelve feet and found the water absolutely roiled opaque. I groped and stumbled, was pricked by urchins and stung by spiculed worms, and twice nudged by soft, squdgey things unseen. I lugged two rocks to the ladder, found I had several small, insignificant oysters, and invited anyone else to take my place. My telephoned comments and epithets had undermined any enthusiasm which might have existed. We found the few I had gathered were tough and consisted more of shell than of meat. So the only asset of memory is that I can say "The last time I dived for oysters in Banderas Bay," etc.

I did not want to leave this first of our bays with only the taste of a mediocre oyster, and so as we headed away from shore I focused ahead. The mouth of the bay is more or less guarded by a group of islands which goes by the name of Las Tres Marietas. This is confusing, for if a native tells you of it with his usual rapidity of speech it sounds exactly like Las Tres Marias, which are larger islands and lie to the north-west, horizon down, but on any small-scale map appear at the very

edge of western Mexico. The Zaca edged up to the largest
and westernmost of the Marietas and then we took to the
motor boat and skiff. We coasted along the whole length of
the island and found no spot less dangerous than another.
The heavy swells from the north-west Pacific were pounding
straight in on the outer side and they then slid around to the
south shore, which should have been the lee, where they rose
and fell with a rush and swirl which would have made landing much too risky.

We then decided to go on to the middle island where we
saw a good-sized sandy beach. The western half was a long,
low, flat tableland which rose by terraces to a lofty ridge cut
into caves and gorges of impressive size. Everywhere brown
boobies swooped and soared and perched on invisible ledges.
The summit was covered with rank green foliage and from
somewhere in the interior a palm grew and showed its topmost fronds in the profile of one narrow gully. (Plate 6.)

I scouted with Pemasa the Samoan toward the sandy beach
and found it unreachable. Surges came in from opposite sides,
and any small boat would be a chip and the sport of the raging whirlpools when the two walls of water met. Just off shore
was a small islet with a great arch through its heart. We went
close and I caught sight of enormous limpets on the rocks. Pe
backed in, and on a favourable lifting swell I leaped to a maze
of slippery, water-worn and eroded outcropping. Before I was
washed off I scrambled up and found encouraging series of
small pools only slightly troubled by intrickling rills from the
highest waves. I called for the rest to come and by luck we all
landed with our apparatus. Pe jumped with an awkward nest
of jars and long-handled nets, lost his balance and fell over

backward, but although quite under water he kept fast his hold on all the stuff and we grabbed his arm and hauled him out with the loss of only one small vial.

We poisoned the pools with copper sulphate and got some grand little fish. One pool was lined with a thick mass of small purple anemones, another with red and a third with an almost solid mat of long-spined urchins. There was a tiny, all-blue fish, unknown to all of us, which evaded every effort at capture. The grapsus crabs, our old sally-lightfoot friends of the Galápagos, were almost solid black with no hint of scarlet.

An adjacent bit of cliff which led up over the natural arch, sloped so slightly that it offered foothold for only a fly or a gecko. Being a member of quite another phylum I was helpless until I exercised what was above the ears; what was supposed to have lifted me above at least the mental level of Diptera and Reptilia. I climbed down to the most sheltered place near the tide level I could find, and with hammer and chisel borrowed from our collecting kit, set to work on the giant limpets. In the skilled use of tools I hold a poor second place to solitary wasps and early cave-men, so I soon yelled for Pe the omnipotent, who can do anything with anything.

When I explained my idea he smiled as only Pe can, and with two or three perfectly directed blows handed me one of the great mollusks, detached but quite unhurt. Quickly, before it could curl tightly up, I reached up and slapped the animal and its three pounds of thick shell flat against the cliff above my head. In a minute or two it had taken hold and settled close to the surface with a grip which no unaided human strength can break. Another and another limpet followed, and by alternating them I soon had a series of foot-

55

holds, slippery and very sloping to be sure, but no more so than the toe-holds cut in ice by mountain climbers. The earliest known limpets flourished some five hundred millions of years ago, and the same extraordinary muscles developed throughout all these generations, now defy the crashing weight and pull of the heaviest surf. My passing light weight must have been of no more account than a footstep of the above-mentioned fly or gecko.

I scrambled at last over the upper rim, aided by stout tufts of coarse grass. The first thing to catch my eye, only a few inches away, was a delightful baby booby, wholly clad in powder-puff down of purest white. There was no sign of fear in his eyes, and for a full minute we gazed at one another, while his parents were diving at me with sharp, bayonet beaks which almost, but not quite, reached and pierced my skull. (Plate 7.)

I crept on through the solid maze of sedge-like grass, flecked with innumerable, small, orange, daisy blossoms. Every few feet was a booby's nest and all well-built of dead grass stems and feathers. Two nests had two eggs each, which were being incubated. For the rest there were about thirty half-grown youngsters, all in identical stage of growth, with long, dark adult feathers sticking through the white down. Only the first chick I had encountered was in true infantile dress. I sent down a rope for cameras and help, and we got an appealing pose of the baby, which I subsequently used for a New Year's card. The nesting birds had yellow-green webs between the toes, but all were the subspecies of Brewster's brown booby.

It was fortunate that I had the rope to descend with, for my molluscan ladder had become restless at being so far away from the water level. How they distinguished this fact, or where to go I cannot tell, but in my absence the rungs had begun to meander on their individual ways, downward, in search of refreshing salt-water spray.

On the back of one of the great mollusks a small humming-bird perched for several seconds, and while a hummingbird traveling for several inches on a living limpet tank contained no tithe of scientific value, it was very probably a new record of transportation.

As I watched my little company embark, instead, as usual, of being out of patience with the physical limitations of the human body I suddenly realized our remarkable adaptations to unusual conditions. Poorly balanced bipeds as we are at best, yet now, as probably a hundred times before on my seven and thirty expeditions, our muscles answered the instant demands of eye and sense of timing. One after the other we stepped quickly into the boat, when a fractional second's delay or acceleration would have meant broken limbs or worse. "And all this," say the comfortable stay-at-homes, "for the sake of a few small fish, some photographs and several pages of hastily jotted down colours, actions and habits" ¡Como no!

We can never tell or write of the indefinable something else, unscientific yet strangely logical and of tremendous importance in our lives, which runs through and over and around all these experiences. This intimate relationship can never be known to those of our planetary fellows who take their risks and dangers at second-hand, who prefer written stories to storms, lectures to lightnings, being to doing. The Fire-siders or Radio Twisters or Cinema Haunters must forever miss the sublimated conceit which follows successful competition with some specialized lesser brother on the earth; as leaping on to a wet, slippery, sea-weeded rock from a bucking skiff, digging in with fingers and toes, and clinging with every muscle and nerve while the following wave crashes overhead. It justifies the grin with which we greet the adjacent limpet and call him brother.

CHAPTER V

ON KNEES TO BEAUTY

CHAMELA BAY is literally not on the chart. It is so small that on a map of the Pacific slope of Mexico of ordinary size it is not even a nick or a wiggle. If somewhere in the vicinity there is the slightest of irregularities this is certain to be Banderas Bay, that great open roadstead thirty miles to the north of the non-indicated Chamela. The inhabitants of Penas, whose picturesque village we left two days ago, have never even heard of this second bay. Yet Chamela has lofty mountains on her brim, perfect sand beaches, islands of superlative beauty and interest, semi-desert jungle and a lagoon which might have stood as the original type of this phenomenon. To me Chamela will always be a very real bit of the world—one which is never dark, for during the three full days which I spent there it was brilliant all day with the circling sun and silvery all night with the round moon. (Plate 8.)

After waiting for a propitious wave—meaning a lower one than its fellows—to cast us ashore, I scrambled up the beach dragging our light pram, and entered into the life of this lovely bay. The beach was wide and pale brown with the finest of sand. Very little wrack lay scattered along the highest of high-tide lines, an occasional bleached tree-trunk, or ivory white pelvis of a pelican. My unosteological artist collected several of these under the impression that they were the skulls of young crocodiles, until we came across the actual skull of a full-grown reptile. The line of shells was a thin one, and I noted that the shells were small and not of noticeable beauty. At this moment I realized that I was again guilty of a habit I am always trying to combat, namely, the egotistical estimates of lesser earthly objects as viewed from the one-fathom height of a human being, with our group of ineffective sense organs carried high aloft, and crowded together within a round, bony case of a head. The instant I became conscious of and shed this attitude and altitude and sank on knees and especially on elbows, I saw that the shells were more beautiful than those of any beach I had ever seen.

Two types of cardium-like ones stand out. In shape they were like the ordinary clam of our New Jersey beaches, roundish, deep-hollowed and with a twist of the summit to right or left according to the dextral or sinistral turn of the valve in question. One species had many fine, concentric lines or ridges on the larger, more recently deposited parts of the shell, which were the older parts as well, as if here the wrinkles of age were included as part of the general beauty, setting off the smooth enamel, proximal cheek of youth.

On these were inscribed all the hieroglyphics and Indian picture writing known to molluscan architecture. To a gatherer of shells (the kindergarten of the university of molluscan interest) a sublimated satisfaction lies in the matching of valves. I found one which showed a perfect inscription of stone-age-man-writing on the "borders of his cave." A large-footed, long-haired hunter (with most incongruous unstone-age-like camera held in front of him) faced a flight of three birds, birds which would delight a surrealist and yet veritable, undeniable birds. All this comfortable imagining came to me as I picked up the valve. I went on, now and then taking a few steps at full height with the viewpoint of a supercilious, unseeing, Lord-of-Creation, then dropping on all-fours again where I could see and handle and appreciate so much better what lay on the sand. I had covered about ten yards and picked up a polished sea-bean which I did not want but which I could not resist handling, smoothing it with sensuous pleasure as one smooths a Chinese rubbing stone. My eye at the same moment caught a half-buried cardium. I turned it over and there was the obverse of my prehistoric camera hunter and his birds. There were two differences. First, in this scene one bird had flown out of the landscape and only a pair remained. Secondly, this valve was quite perfect, while the very tip of the other revealed the mode of death of the architect; a sinister hole of that deadly enemy, the Drill. (Plate 9.)

I could go on and describe in detail a whole gallery of snail portraiture but I kept wondering who was my primal ancestor whose eyes could first stereoscopically separate into three planes an image delineated in the flat. A dog or a bird will recognize its moving reflection in a window or a mirror and attempt friendship or give battle, but an immovable photographic or painted resemblance arouses no emotion. So we must add to the discovery of the use of clubs and tools, and the utilization of fire, the esthetic revelation of stereoscopy. The exact alignment of the two eyes, side by side looking forward, was of course a necessary physical condition. And this binocular vision was also based on the evolution of bravery and self-sufficiency. For an animal with monocular vision is usually a pursued one, like a rabbit, while a pursuer, such as an owl, usually has forward looking, binocular eyes.

As I sat absorbed in my etching in lime of birds and trees and primitive man, I thought of the first artist genius of the Dordogne Caves, and especially of Ung, the friend of my friend Kipling, because

Later he pictured an aurochs—later he pictured a bear—
Pictured the saber-toothed tiger dragging a man to his lair—
Pictured the mountainous mammoth, hairy, abhorrent, alone—
Out of the love that he bore them, scriving them clearly on bone.

One of the advantages of a snail's armature over the skeleton of a man is that one may read as he looks, all of the individual's past history, and the passage from the beauty of youth to the charm of old age is there spread out like a map or scroll for all to see, and indeed, to interpret, if we could ever come to consider the shell less as a coloured mineral, an abstract phenomenon of lime, than as an animal artifact. Again we are conscious of the luxury and comfort of man's life; it is easier for us to pick up shells on the beach than to labour with the dredge or wade in the shallows and deeps for the architects, the owners that were. We know little or nothing of their craftsmanship, of the changing needs, the successes and failures of these submarine castles and huts, these homes. A consummate simile would be to be contented to study the fragments of fossil paleolithic human skeletons when we might, by going to considerable trouble and undergoing discomforts, find and observe living representatives of these early tribes. It is indeed as unreasonable as to take the pelvic bone of the pelican and study that, and never look up

62

4. *Young Bull Sea-elephant.* He ponders his next move in life, and dreads it.

in the sky and watch the birds themselves. Yet even in the case of the bleached bone among the shells, the moment we concentrate new things come to light.

We pick up one of the said pelican pelvises. Its intricacy and delicacy of carving allies it to a Japanese netsuke. Fore and aft are one or two free vertebrae, while the center is a single bone perforated and loopholed with fenestra of various shapes and sizes. We look closer and find the free backbones continued into the ivory matrix; we can count on and on and suddenly the significance is apparent. As in the human pelvis the ossification and consolidation of this part of the backbone is to provide support for an erect, bipedal position. In the bird's bone which we have just picked up the openings are very distinct. We can detect evidences of fourteen vertebrae which are concerned in this bony palimpsest. A hundred or more millions of years before this visit of mine to Chamela, these bones, in an ancestor of the pelican, were all free and movable, with a pair of feathers attached to each; that being the age when the long lizard tail had sprouted feathers but not yet consolidated; before the time when gliding gave place to true flying and soaring.

And having delivered myself of this dramatic but fairly heavy bit of philosophy I suddenly sat down on the hot sand and watched the long lines of pelicans passing overhead, their shadows flicking over my face. I saw their twinkling eyes, and the slight uplift at the corner of the immense beak, which always seemed to me to indicate a sense of humour, a smile which was almost ready to burst into a guffaw. Supreme in their power of flight, they looked down at my earth-bound body and appeared to say: "All right, Wise Man, suppose our

63

5. *Sea-lions of San Benito.* They rush to meet us from their home on Middle Island. A few months later all were slain to make canned dog food.

pelvis does symbolize the tail of Archaeopteryx—so what?"
A little embarrassed, I looked about me, ascended to my full
six feet and, having no answer, stalked silently away.

Some animal relationships seem scarcely possible, judged
by external characters. It is difficult to believe in the cousin-
ship of sloths and anteaters, and equally incredible that pelicans and boobies are bound together structurally even more
closely than are their four toes by a single web. From the silent smile of the former I was abruptly distracted by a sudden
uproar, near shore, of raucous squawks. As unexpectedly as a
tropical squall there appeared, just beyond the breakers, two
dense clouds of brown and white boobies. The simile is not
wholly fanciful for the cloud-flocks were precipitating hundreds of individual birds which fell, plummet-like, in a continuous rain. From the mass of spray thrown up, equal numbers of boobies were simultaneously emerging, labouring obliquely but swiftly up, to where, after a vigorous swallow and
a narrow circling, they again joined the dense throng, and
prepared for another dive and another fish.

Also like clouds, the two masses moved slowly along the
shore until the squawking died away in the distance. I saw
some fish of medium size floating in through the surf and
salvaged several wounded and dead ones. They were silvery,
moderately deep, with well-forked tails. The eyes were larger
than is usual in six-inch fish, but far from justifying their popu-
lar names of goggle-eyed jacks or goggling scad. I prefer the
more euphonious title of *Trachurops crumenopthalmus.*

Tens of thousands of these small jacks were swimming
close to the surface and, for ten minutes at least, the host
seemed quite undisturbed by the fact that hundreds were

slipping down the throats of the diving boobies. Life to the boobies and gannets is a seriously fierce thing. To our human viewpoint, there seems no relaxation as in the pelicans, no humour either in their existence or at the corners of their terrible, spear-like beaks.

We found Chamela good collecting ground, but the unadventurous assembling of crabs, mollusks and fish has no right in a general account. The thrill and excitement of new species, or much more creditably the solution or discovery of some habit or peculiar structure or organ—this is for technical papers. What stands out in the memory of this place is the lagoon and its bird life. In bay after bay we were to find high sand dunes and, on the farther side instead of a gradual change into arid cactus and palm scrub, the sand would slope down to an expanse of mangrove-bound, brackish water. At Chamela we had no trouble in pulling our folding boat up and over the dune and into the lagoon. Hardly had I started paddling when a grandfather of a crocodile slipped off a mudbank and sounded in a cloud of spray. Later we saw several small ones doing their drifting-log specialty and watching us through their sinister, cat-like eyes.

Slowly, paddling below surface, with no sound and hardly a ripple, we wound our way up a meandering bayou, then through a hundred yards of lake, and out again into shaded mangrove water paths. Only in the flying cage in our Zoological Park have I seen water birds so abundant, so tame and of so many kinds.

Always in the sky overhead the vultures wove their wakeless patterns, proving to our unseeing eyes that the air is a very solid thing, and that gravity can be made to seem non-existent.

A great blue heron and a trio of ringed kingfishers flew across our bows. Eighteen cormorants rose splashing from the lagoon, but instead of beating, duck-like, straight off to other feeding grounds, they began spiraling, gaining altitude and finally joining a cluster of specks which my high-power glasses resolved into pelicans and frigatebirds.

Herons were everywhere, some a bit awkward among the branches, with beautiful chestnut-rufous neck plumes, bearing the utterly absurd name of Louisiana herons; little blues, some in juvenal pure white and others parti-coloured; snowy egrets in a mist of plumes, and with the daintiest of golden slippers and black stockings; their more sedate and larger cousins, with another meaningless name—American egret; friendly little greens climbing skillfully among the branches, and raucous-voiced night herons. Strangest and most tropical were the night herons' near relations, well-named boat-billed herons. They watched us fearlessly, down their great mandibles, and flew only at a ten-foot dead line. Running along the muddy banks, yet immaculate in every feather, were the waders; willets, plover, godwits, spotted and solitary sandpipers, slender-legged stilts, and best of all a flock of Hudsonian curlews. The sweet, stirring calls of the latter put heat and mangroves and tropics out of mind, and replaced them with far-reaching tundra and bleak landscapes and the bracing, icy air of the far north. I loved the wild notes, but I was grateful for the warmth of this southland. White ibises stood out blatantly in contrast with the dark green leaves, and vermilion flycatchers burned as brightly against the blue sky. There were others which filled in ornithological chinks around this foreground of dominant species. The whole experience was one which cannot be imparted in words, but suggested only, in the hope of arousing complementary memories in the reader.

The few black hawks were on the lookout only for snails and lizards; to attract and hold the attention of the vultures one had to be ill or dead; the drifting crocodiles could be detected in time by the dullest avian eye. Indeed, there seemed to be no dangers, but abundant food and room for all. No wonder the happy family of lagoon birds reached five and twenty kinds, and hundreds of individuals.

CHAPTER VI

THE WHITE MORPHO OF TENACATITA

EARLY in the morning of the twentieth of November we left Chamela and before noon were in the next bay which bore the pleasant name of Tenacatita. In approach, shape, size, lagoon and general feeling it was a slightly smaller replica of the more northern bay, but in animal life it was a comparative desert. We realized this soon after we landed and in vain sought for a reason. An unusual number of vultures might have been significant had we not known that this was a wholly misleading phenomenon in the present respect. A few egrets and pelicans sat about disconsolately, while a fish or two leaped languidly, and the mangroves offered abundant shelter to non-existent tenants.

Finding the shore and sand barren of our desires, we made several hauls with the dredge across the bay. A few good fish and shells were taken, but the last haul gave us a pile of beauty and interest. Up from a depth of two hundred and forty feet came a heap of more than a hundred small sponges in the form of rounded pads. Some were half an inch across, others two and a half inches, but all were flattened, pad or biscuit shaped. Near the edge of each was a slightly flaring hole, the rim yellowish, in contrast with the inner walls which were olive green like the rest of the sponge. From each of these, at one time or another, peered forth a hermit crab. I found one where the shell and the crab were half exposed, only the posterior beginning to be enveloped by the animal dune. In parts of this bay the bottom must be almost covered with these little animated pads.

The crab, apparently, selects a small shell which fits his spiral abdomen, and goes on about his business. One day there seems a greater drag than usual. It is not a bit of weed or a pebble of sand in the way, and if his eyes are anywhere near as sharp as they seem to be, he soon distinguishes a green growth astern. We know nothing of his reaction, but we do know that in a great many cases he disregards it. It is no more to him than the emerald algae in the fur of the sloth, or the viridity of the old frock-coat of an indigent colored preacher.

Perhaps the hermit tries to trim the sponge, but fails. It grows steadily, probably thriving the more as it approaches the crab, for the crumbs from the meals of the latter, the bits which drift astern, must serve as welcome nourishment, being caught in the induced current in the heart of the lowly animal colony. At any rate the sponge thrives and slowly enwraps the shell and spreads out on all sides. For some reason it thins out ahead, due perhaps to the attrition caused by the constant progress of the crab over rough ground. But the size and weight of a two-inch sponge, as well as lesser ones, must be tremendous compared with the size and strength of the hermit.

In the course of time the crab outgrows the shell and in the usual run of life it would search about and find another. As a matter of fact, I found a few of these crab-sponge relationships in Inez Bay, far to the north, two years before, and of these I wrote: "The weight of growth . . . would finally clog and hamper the movements of the little guest and force his removal to a new home." This I took for granted as I wished to preserve the few specimens intact. However, I dissected twenty or more of the sponge pads from Tenacatita and discovered several interesting things. In more than half, the crab was outrageously large for the size of the shell. The whorls no more than covered the terminal segment and hook which is the lock and key to its domicile. All the rest of the hermit was outside the shell but inside the sponge. The inevitable growth had been put to use, and between the mouth of the shell and the outer world was a smooth tunnel of exactly the calibre and rifling of the crab's twisted body. This was sometimes as much as a half inch in length, and one crab, at least, had a mass of scarlet eggs attached to the depths of the sponge tunnel. All this completely refuted my assumption which I have quoted from my first Zaca expedition.

In three instances, two hermits and two shells were found in the same sponge. In each of these cases the sponge was large, and one of the hermits was dead, entombed in the living mesh, while the second, a large and healthy crab, was happily settled in shell and sponge. The little tragedy could be pictured; the sponge beginning to encroach upon them when they were very small. Then each began pulling hard, to proceed on its individual way, one to the north, the other to the southwest of the sponge's compass. Southwest lost out— it could not produce sufficient attrition, enough rubbing against other shells, rocks, whatever impeded progress. So the sponge grew on and on, and finally threw its verdant veil of death over shell and crab, the whole contraption being dragged along toward the north by the other, stronger crustacean.

About one fourth of the entire lot had shells still inhabited by the original owner, but all of these were very small sponges and I doubt if the mollusk could long endure the closing in of the green growth. I have spoken of the position of the hermit crabs on the rim but a little beneath, on the under side, exactly where it could get the best grip for walking. On the upper side of the sponge pad, and invariably toward the hinder end, was the large sponge osculum, providing the whole colony with exit for waste matter. It made the whole affair look like a single organism. The crab was certaintly perfectly protected by the enveloping sheath of inedible tissue; the sponge got free transportation which brought to it an increased amount of oxygen and food; it flourished on the remnants of the crab's food, and the whole miracle provided an immeasurable amount of pleasure and material for thought to at least one wondering scientist.

Before we left the bay I took one walk along the shore, and was cheered by hints of the beginning of truly tropical organisms. On my way I met a friendly, aged Mexican, who swept off his great sombrero in a courtly bow, reminiscent of old Spain. He was riding a diminutive horse and leading a loaded burro and her foal, or whatever a baby donkey is called. He said there were only three families living anywhere in the vicinity of the bay. His hat band was woven of bright beads worked into stylized figures which appeared half Mexican, half Aztec. Besides an embroidered waistcoat and tattered chaps, he sported a beautifully tooled and inlaid saddle of leather, a quirt, gun, lasso, machete, and a cow's horn rudely carved, from which, at my request, he drew forth tremulous, lugubrious wails. He was so proud of the effort that I applauded with many *Bravos!* and he graciously obliged with an encore. The uproar frightened a flock of green parrakeets, and this appearance of wild life made me bid him a hasty *Adios,* and I passed on along the almost invisible trail. Thorn-scrub and cactus spines reached out and caught me on any diversion to one side, and when a clear space invited, sliding, over-balanced rocks and stones were always ready to tip me toward some bit of nature's barbed wire.

A short distance from the bay I came to a dried dropping of the caballero's horse, and flicked it over, with the instinct of any good coleopterist. My reward was a glorious, burnished green scarab, and as I was bottling it, two more spiraled down, the engines of their whirring wings giving forth that fascinating deep roaring hum which, in the tropics, should never be disregarded. One of the newcomers was a big male beetle, outdoing a rhinoceros, for he bore one long and two short, stout, curved horns.

I have a favorite saying that, in the tropics, I am always on the lookout for a twenty-four-inch ant, or its equivalent, and I have found several equivalents. Herein lies one great advantage of ignorance, for if I were thoroughly familiar with all known forms of animal life I could never be surprised into incredulous amazement. This may be momentary, lasting only until the more prosaic part of my mind redefines or catalogues the thing in question. As I stood up from preserving my precious scarabs, I saw my twofootantorwhathaveyou, for a giant *white* Morpho butterfly fluttered toward me along the trail. My companion handed me a net and I made a swoop, but it never even descended, for the good fairy of the butter-fly reached out ten spiny fingers from a candelabra cactus and held fast the mesh of the netting in mid-air. While I strug-gled, the beautiful creature floated down to the dung at my feet, alighted for a moment and then drifted away.

As I disentangled the remnants of the net, I said, in my ecstasy of ignorance, "So there are white Morphos!" A mu-seum lepidopterist if present would have murmured "A very perfect specimen of Morpho polyphemus."

As usual I prayed fervently, but unconsciously, as I walked on, and before I returned to the bay my supplication was answered. The same, or another insect alighted near me, on the edge of a damp bit of earth, uncoiled its tongue and drank, its wonderful wings heeling over in the gentle breeze. It made no attempt to fly when I lowered my threadbare net, and vanished against the white material so completely that I feared it had again escaped. It was very much like the train of a white peacock in that the eye-spots so characteristic of its family were all present, but concealed except in certain lights, like watered silk. In general it was pearly, iridescent white with a series of small eyes, fashioned from a few irides-cent scales, and an orange ring on the hind wings.

Familiar as I was only with the green and blue Morphos of tropical jungles, this unexpected marvel of a snowy butter-fly, at home in a semi-arid land of cactus, was like an appari-tion. Something deep within me had been aroused and played upon, exactly as had happened at my first view of the rings of Saturn, of my first active volcano, of a wild monkey, and the moon-crossing flock of what to me, for an appreciable

73

length of time, were pterodactyls. When my time comes, if I could choose my mode of death, it would assuredly be of sudden heart failure from some unexpected, unpredictable sight such as one of these.

My last note of Tenacatita was made in the evening from the deck of the Zaca. After sunset a great gibbous moon rose gray and ghostly from behind the serried ranges of mountains, themselves weird in that light. As it rose, the moon gained in substance and goldness. A chorus of insects and frogs came from the land, evanescent and difficult to place. At midnight Templeton called me on deck, and the mystery of the chorus was solved. Well up above the Zaca we could see in the beam of the searchlight a host of little birds flying about, petrels, whose twitterings, now focused by the added sense of sight, were what we had thought was a chorus from land. As I finally closed my eyes in my bunk I thought of Tenacatita, as I always shall, as the home of my silvery white Morpho ghost of a butterfly.

CHAPTER VII

NIGHT FIESTA IN MANZANILLO

OUR first real Mexican town was sound asleep at half-past two on the hot afternoon of *Domingo*, November twenty-first. It was Manzanillo, and it was one big siesta. We, like "mad dogs and Englishmen" disregarded the blazing heat, and clambered up and down the hills, to no evident result scientifically, but to the betterment of our evaporation pores. To these steep slopes clung rather pitiful dwelling places, fashioned by peons too poor to include a patio. But in place of this enclosed heart of beauty, there was always a box or gasoline tin with some flowering plant culled from somewhere, often only a wizened geranium, dusty and droopy, but with a brave blossom. A scattered sound of pigs was all that greeted us, rushing out from beneath the huts of wattled clay. Yet each house had a rough cage from which a sleepy parrakeet or tanager watched us through one somnolent eye. Indolent snakebirds perched in the mangroves, and great yellow flycatchers rested on bare branches, too hot and lazy even to *kiskadee!* for us. Another tropical note was a few heliconia butterflies whose slow, languid flight emphasized the general Sunday torpidity. After almost falling through a disreputable bridge we returned to the *Zaca*.

After dinner we again went ashore and the double, magical wand of coolness and night had worked wonders. The place

75

seethed with life, noise and activity. We went to the main plaza and drank doubtful cerveza from dubious glasses. At an adjoining table three desperados, armed at every possible point, sucked ice-cream sodas through wilted, second-hand straws, and obviously made the drinks last as long as possible. Their attention was wholly concerned with two of the three double lines of promenaders, passing and repassing. The center stream, consisting of men only, resembled a dark line in the spectrum, bounded by two intensely brilliant ones, for the two remaining files of Mexican senoritas were ablaze with gorgeous colors and patterns.

Five bands were playing at once and all well within the sound of each other's instruments. One, in a bus, advertising a cinema, "The Robin Hood of Mexico," provided the elements of crescendo and diminuendo in this quintet of orchestras, as the bus approached the plaza or receded. The ensemble, although occasionally overpowering, was rather pleasant. Two bands, vying with one another, would have been most objectionable, one's sense of rhythm being monopolized first by one, then the other. But when five are operating simultaneously one has no choice but to attend to the pandemonium as a whole, and actually it was not unpleasant, and not overwhelmingly noisy. Many of the more strident chords seemed to soften or obliterate each other.

In front of a large cafeteria, in a cleared space, was the second orchestra, a sort of hybrid Spanish-cum-jazz affair. Here, for the small sum of fifty centavos, one could dance apparently all night, with intervals of relaxing and drinking. Strange tangos were the speciality of this group and for five minutes we watched a small urchin perform amazingly, with hands held tightly behind his back, a cross between a rumba and a dervish whirl. In the center of the plaza was the official band, which provided classical entertainment, under the baton of a maestro with the incredible name of Jesus C. Pilato. His directing had such temperament that the sound effects either dominated all the four other assemblages, or else became utterly inaudible. From where we sat this resulted in the quaint appearance of a director and his musicians in full play, making motions wholly out of tempo with some strident hot jazz tune, which for the moment held the upper hand.

From a large tent at one side of the plaza still another band alternately blared forth, and became silent while a villainous looking barker roared through a tin loud speaker, that at nine-thirty of the clock the grand drama "La Dama de las Camelias" would be presented, with the assurance that with the part of Margarita played by the *applaudida* Luisa Velasco, it was indubitably "*¡Exito seguro!*" and as to its respectability, it was "*Espectaculo Propio para Familias.*"

Thus assured, we decided to attend, and for a peso each were led to the *luneta*, a line of string-seated chairs. Along the sides of the tent were the *grados* (apparently Mexican for bleachers) well filled with, judging by facial expressions and costumes, Indians, cutthroats, Aztecs, pirates, babies at the breast or not, conquistadores and ladies of Spain. Every face was a study, some scarred and stamped with the fear of life, others with profiles straight from a Mayan stele, now and then a very lovely face, but all vitally absorbed in everything. The center aisle was, for some reason, beloved of stray dogs, which crept under the tent, and performed absorbing, acrobatic feats of flea-scratching.

77

A trio, violin, piano and drums, played the overture to "Poet and Peasant" and did it very well. Then the curtain went up knee-high to the actor on the stage, and simultaneously the government band just outside, broke forth in something of Wagnerian force. The curtain descended abruptly and noisily, and soon the plaza band stopped and chose some softer theme which allowed the voices of the actors to be heard.

We stayed through two scenes, performed most heartily by the leading actress. Amid a nation and an audience of brunettes, the observation that Luisa Velasco was blonde is an understatement. She reminded me somewhat of Lillian Russell, but a Lillian Russell with an added number of pounds avoirdupois which I hesitate to estimate. She was clothed in a dress of cloth of silver, and one was impelled to the belief that the only possible method of introduction into it was by a process of pouring. The gasp of genuine awe from the *grados* when the silver Margarita, after rather audibly mounting the back-curtain stairs, appeared on the stage, must have meant that the word Madonna took on, for many, a new and a very definite connotation.

The stage was ridiculously small, and when Margarita crossed L to R the floor bent alarmingly. Yet she must have been an unusually talented actress in her prime, and nothing in the embarrassingly limited surroundings affected her performance. She was very good, and as wholly undisturbed by her audience of desperados, Indians, babies and dogs as well as itinerant gringos as if she were giving a command performance. One of the minor actors spilled a glass of wine on the seat of the only chair, and in the course of two long

78

6. *Brown Booby on His Look-out.* Beneath the cactus, on the ground, are his nest and young.

speeches Luisa deftly dropped her handkerchief, a news-paper and the cover from a small table on to the chair before she trusted her frock to its damp seat. The clothes of the leading man were many sizes too big for him, yet he skillfully shook his hands free of the enveloping sleeves when gestures demanded their appearance. Wherever Dumas had written in a kiss, the resounding smack was greeted by the occupants of the *grados* with a hearty murmur of approval, while some voice would petition *"¡Un otro!"* But the attention of the entire audience never wavered and we led the applause with enthusiasm and fervor. One very noticeable thing was the perfect Castilian Spanish diction of the leading members of the cast. There would have been no z's in Luisa's *cerveza*, if she would condescend to speak of so lowly a beverage.

As I made my way back to the yacht I thought of Luisa Velasco with great pity. The sunset of such an actress is not pleasant, and yet the sincerity of the whole—bands, perform-ance, audience—made it all admirable. And under trying con-ditions she held her audience, even though only a fraction could have known what it was all about; Bernhardt could not have done more.

When we reached the Zaca this same evening, the sight at the submarine night light kept us concentrated for a long time. About the glow of the bulb was the usual dense mass of small fry, all going clockwise, full speed. Close outside their orbit was another zone of life, outdoing even the rings of Saturn, for this circle was moving anti-clockwise. For a time I had no idea what the fish were, for to our dim eyesight, looking down from the deck, there appeared to be thousands of the thinnest lines of silver, all shooting ahead in a wheel

79

7. *Baby Booby Posing on His Marieta Home.* He is still in his immaculate nestling down.

of life, at a mad, furious pace. A dozen of these outsiders suddenly turned obliquely inward, each seized a small fish and banked outward again. As they moved from their place they turned sideways, and the lines became full silvery plaques— moonfish—the thinnest, roundest, silveriest things imaginable. Usually one is seen, or at most a few together, but here all the ocean seemed to have given up its hordes of lunar constellations, and the multitude had become magnetized by our little glow. (Plate 10.)

I pulled the lamp slowly above the water, and the moonfish closed in, overrunning the smaller, inner fry, looking like diminutive replicas of all moon reflections in the water since time began. Finally, they broke the surface, forgetting their hunger and everything, impelled to follow upward by the luminous spell of the strange gleam. When the light descended again they quieted down and resumed their eternal whirling. We took a flashlight photograph and this sudden, momentary increase of illumination frightened them all into the surrounding darkness, but in two minutes all were back. When I held the light clear of the surface for three minutes the multitude of fry had gone for good, but the moonfish then closed in, and when I went down to my cabin the thousands upon thousands filled every visible area of water. A last glance ashore showed the last lights of Manzanillo flickering out, and I thought of Luisa Velasco in her cloth of silver, and I thought of the mad, but equally brilliant moonfish, and I rejoiced in the grand thing which we call diversity of interest in this life of ours on the earth. (Plate 11.)

A quick run ashore the following morning showed Manzanillo rather threadbare, without its tinsel veneer of night

and electric light, and we saw many of our new friends somewhat the worse for wear. There was no bank so I changed
some money at the house of a Portuguese who unlocked the
padlock of his rusty safe with a nail. The test of a Latin
American town is its market and this one was small and poor.
This was one of our bays, to be sure, lagoon and all, but in
the blatant glare of day we found that man had left it little
of visible charm.

We had difficulty in getting permission to dredge in the
harbor as we left, because the year before a Japanese battleship had asked to be allowed to drag for the body of a sailor
who had fallen overboard, and then proceeded to take a complete series of soundings. The patient display and explanation
of the published Manzanillo chart whereon were recorded
every possible sounding which could be made, together with
judicious use of liquid palliatives, soon cleared us of suspicion
and made us free of the entire Mexican coast.

The first dredge came up quite barren except for sundry
bottles and tins and a small, much annoyed puffer. But the
second of twenty minutes in one hundred and eighty feet,
proved incredibly rich. Among a crowd of other organisms
there were sixty of the pearl-bearing singing fish,[1] and at
least twenty species of rare crabs. We could not finish the
sorting and describing even with the deck lights, late at night,
so stopped dredging and put to sea from sheer physical inability to tackle another haul.

[1] Zaca Venture, page 155.

CHAPTER VIII

FROM BABY SAILFISH TO LA ESPERANZA

THE day before Thanksgiving we steamed slowly past a little, black islet with an equally diminutive lantern-sized light, too small even to be mentioned in the *West Coast Pilot*. Before us opened a beautiful bay with a euphonious name—Sihuatenejo (and please don't spoil it. Pronounced with Anglo-Saxon inflexion it is a horror; give it the full Castilian sonority, see-hua-tay-nay-ho).

We would have been quite content to sit on the deck of the *Zaca* and absorb the satisfying, harmonious beauty of the place. The setting was of undulating mountains, purple and gray, in places dropping sheer hundreds of feet, elsewhere with a thousand fingers of candelabra cactus pointing to blue heaven. Rough capes jutted out, crags fraying into detached rocks before plunging into the bay itself. Gravelly beaches of pink and buff, with stretches of surf-lined sand of a dozen shades made almost too perfect a picture. A small village, shaded with curving palm trees, was close beside a tiny rio, and to one side lay the quiet expanse of the inevitable lagoon.

We came, we saw, we investigated, and we departed thoroughly disappointed. The very fact of the meagerness or absence of birds, insects, mollusks and shore fish would have been of real scientific interest, provided we had had the time to find out why. To the north and south were bays, similar in outward aspect, but abounding in the living creatures we sought.

As is so often the case, it was by accident that we found the one hidden vein of precious life. Discouraged, I scuffed through the shallow water at low tide, over rocks and sandy mud. And then something began to snap and crackle beneath my feet. I found I was walking on the topmost branches of a large patch of coral. It was not lovely coral, it was brown and dirty, and all that was visible was an endless stretch of separate, thick nubbins which broke off easily. Stamping a small area loose, I caught sight of something scarlet moving about, a crab, then a bright-colored fish.

I returned with the news and Templeton, with two men, went off and loaded several large tin wash-boilers full of solid coral clumps, torn up by the roots. We improvised a rock-breaking, prisoners' circle, and for hours hammered the coral apart and picked out what we found within. Sihuatenejo had not let us down altogether, and elsewhere I shall tell of the wealth of interest to be found in the submarine coral folk, inhabiting a world hidden and apart, safe from everything except scientists. Still hammering away at dusk, we felt the vibration of the anchor chain coming in, and the diesels started their low throbbing. The Zaca swung around and put to sea.

At the light that night, fish were rare, coming singly, flashing about for a moment and usually disappearing down the throats of several sizes of squids. We had to be swift with the nets to get ahead of the mollusks.

I went to my cabin fairly early to write up the day's notes.

At about 11.30 o'clock a dripping net at the end of a long handle was swung in the door and dangled between my face and my written page. I looked down, and then at the staring eyes of Ben, the sailor in charge of the fishing launch, whose special province was the preparations for the capture of tuna, marlin and sailfish. The acme of life, the supreme ideal of achievement of the game fisherman is to capture, on some absurdly slender, pliant rod, and with the thinnest thread line physically possible, to hook and to land a Record Fish, meaning a fish perhaps a half-inch or a quarter of a pound longer or heavier than any fish landed by any other human being, dead or alive. A giant of the same species, ahead of all Records, which has died a natural death and been washed ashore, holds the fisherman's interest not for a moment.

I looked down into the shallow net, and I yelled: "The World's Record Pacific Sailfish!" Zane Grey was scornful of my claim when he heard of it, but why cannot I start a new type of fishing record? The smallest fish?

As a matter of fact my dominant interest was that it was a young sailfish, nearer the unknown larva, nearer the unknown egg; a specimen which might help in telling us something of the evolution, and of the relationship of sailfish to their fossil and living congeners.

Later, when I came to examine the little fish, I found that while superficially it was much like the full-grown one, yet this baby must live a wholly different sort of life. Instead of a slashing broadsword the elongate beak was slender and delicate, and furnished with very conventional rows of small teeth, unlike the short, stout denticles of the parent sailfish, scattered all about like the crocodile teeth which savages set

84

in the head of their war club. The small body was covered
with elaborate, close-set scales which bore no resemblance to
the half-sunken scutes of the adult fish. In its stomach were
copepods, minute shrimps of sorts, so daintily captured and
swallowed that they could readily be identified even as to
species.

So the Bay posthumously redeemed itself, at least by proxy:
LABEL: 1 young specimen of *Istiophorus greyi* Jordan and
Hill, Length 84 mm. (3¼ inches); Taken at night light, 11:30
P.M. November 23rd, 1937; 23 miles off Sihuatenejo Bay.
Cat. No. 27,140.

The only simile which comes to mind, furnishing the same
extremes as did these Pacific Bays, is a revolving stage. I have
sat in an audience and seen the hero and heroine wrecked on
a desert island, with more or less convincing tropic moon,
wobbly palms, and a shimmering sea done with mirrors. After
satisfactory action the curtain descends, and within a few
seconds the succeeding act is presented, perhaps amid the
glitter and music of a ballroom in some city thousands of
miles away from the desert isle.

So it was from our box seats on the *Zaca*. The sinking sun
drew the curtain of night over the panorama of wild mountains of Sihuatenejo, the rocks and sand, the cactus and thorn
scrub, the deserted shore and barren headlands. And then,
after an intermission of quiet steaming, the same sun rose on
a new headland and there came into view the beautiful city
of Acapulco—a long line of wharves and buildings along the
water front, then tier upon tier of houses covering the hills,
with the most pretentious dwellings on the very summits.

A few minutes after we landed a new friend came into my

85

life, a man with the sonorous name of Wolfgang von Schoen-
born, whose mission in life seemed to be to do kindnesses to
strangers and to like it. He also sold plots on the side and
built houses on them, but when he found that I desired
neither plot nor residence, he seemed relieved and forthwith
devoted himself to unrequited amenities. He possessed a car
whose tires must have been covered with vacuum cups; at
least it shared the ambulatory feats of a house-fly. It seemed
to have entered into a cosmic alliance for the amelioration
of gravitation. It climbed and twisted about the sharpest of
curves, and stopped at will on the steepest of grades. Yet I
can recall no sound or whisper of gears or brakes. We wound
up the nearest mountain with a speed and constant shift of
view which I had deemed possible only in a high-powered
plane. At one spot I admired a blossom and we stopped in
full speed with what appeared to be two wheels in mid-air,
quite overhanging a precipice. After that my approvals were
inaudible murmurs.

At last we came out upon the tiny summit, and for minutes were speechless with the great beauty. The earth and the
sea were at a vast distance below us. Acapulco had shrunk
into a parti-colored blotch, human beings having long since
vanished altogether. The rest defied any verbal description,
the range upon range of mountains, cutting into the deep
blue sky; the still bluer ocean shifting into emerald shallows,
separated from the warm buff sand by the veriest thread of a
seam of alabaster—all that reached our eyes of the mighty
Pacific breakers. The only living thing was a vulture, sublimated, floating majestically below us, a black silhouette, doing

86

what no man-made machine could do and caring nothing about it. (Plate 12.)

I walked to the very brink, thankful to my companions for their silence, and looked down. I saw something so unexpected that it was not a shock. I shifted my gaze from the enthralling beauty of earth, sea and sky, and on a little flat ledge a few feet down I saw two well-dressed Mexicans. They were sitting facing one another, and they too were silent, wrapped in their own thoughts. But on the face of one was a worried frown; something in what he saw disturbed him. Throughout whole minutes I watched, fascinated, and neither man moved or spoke. Only the frown remained. They were playing chess, and the Frown had just lost his second bishop.

I stepped back quietly; I entered our car, and we began to descend. So far as I know, the two astonishing Mexicans may still be there, still silent, still motionless on the mountain top.

Science was, of necessity, in abeyance while we took on board fuel for man and ship. As I look back in memory at Acapulco, my most vivid recollection is of four places of entertainment. The first was the Hotel Mirador, which was marred only by a sudden eruption of tourists. A mediocre orchestra egged these sad intruders on to the dance floor, and their futile but complacent attempts at rumbas and tangos were one of the saddest sights I remember in Acapulco. The hotel itself represented a perfect hostelry, the acme of food, drink and vista, materializing in an unforgettable Thanksgiving repast. Behind the great bar was a well-executed, vivid mural of twenty-odd of the largest and best known native fishes, dominated by the striking, life-size figure of a famous native fisherman.

87

Another hotel was considerably smaller, and there I made the acquaintance of something of which I had heard but never seen. On the walls of the dining room were several examples of Votive Art. They were from the old church at Taxla, a village not far away, quite undisturbed by tourists or any modern influence. Among the natives the shrine had become famous from the number of reputed cures which had taken place. It was the custom for every beneficiary to sit down and depict his accident, disease or more casual trouble as best he could, upon canvas or wood. The character of these was unbelievable, and in some ways recalled the treatment of Aztec art.

One showed the heroine in the act of throwing herself off her horse just as the animal slipped and slid over the rim of a precipice. A little trail of smoke led up to frame the particular saint who had reached out and saved her. A second picture showed a beloved cat which had swallowed a needle but, by the intervention of some veterinarially disposed saint, had been saved. A third represented an awkward house boy who had fallen into the patio fountain but after having broken some ornamental plants had been fished out miraculously and rescued from drowning. Near Monte Carlo, at the monastery of Laghet there are some twenty-five hundred similar works of art, one unanatomical but touching representation of Vierginie Ciccion who at a most tender age was dragged from her cradle by a wild boar and saved by saintly intervention.

A steep step down the Acapulcan social ladder was a haunt of reputedly sinister types of criminals, where we had excellent beer. We also enjoyed pleasant and informative conversations with the above-mentioned gangsters who differed not

at all, as far as we could see, from any average Mexican. Much
the same applies to American criminals I have met!

Late at night we struck social bottom at "La Esperanza,"
an unforgettable experience. Wolfgang palavered at the front
door in a dark side street before it was opened for us. Then
we passed through two empty rooms and came out on a large
patio shut in with adobe walls painted a bright pink. Great
palms stretched high up through the moonlight, the fronds
rustling faintly, and the stars twinkling beyond. Along one
side was seated a row of some twenty girls, dressed in bright
red and blue satin, while groups of men drank at tables on
the other side, men all in white, each in a sombrero of individual crown or brim. Here was the lowest stratum, a meeting
place of quite unmoral persons, with impeccable good manners, showing no resentment, nor even curiosity at our presence.

While we sipped some strange concoction, a marimba band
struck up, which in excellence of timbre and rhythm ex-
ceeded any I had ever heard. All the lights went out except
a tiny blue bulb on each palm trunk, and one by one the
peons, with the stride of conquistadores, crossed the patio,
and for the sum of ten centavos, claimed a dance from Miss
Blue or Miss Red Satin. The dancing was on a par with the
music, equal to any first-class exhibition Spanish dancing in
the north.

The whole affair seemed most serious; there was no laugh-
ter, almost no talking. The moment the music ended, the
lights came on and the dancing pairs separated instantly wherever they might be, each person walking to his place.

The proprietor was an astonishing person. His walk was a

mincing, graceful swing, he was slender, but apparently with muscles like steel, yet with plucked eyebrows, great lustrous, made-up eyes, and lashes for which any Hollywood Star would have pledged her soul. He came to our table and drank a liqueur, courteous, wholly unselfconscious, most intelligent. He knew almost all the fishes we mentioned and asked if they would all go to our museums.

He had just come out of jail into which he seemed to be cast at irregular intervals by the powers that be, and fined forty pesos for keeping a dance hall of this character. This last time, after three days, the girls had chipped in and paid half his fine so "La Esperanza" could open again. After each dance he went down the line and collected half the fee, so that the share of each girl was about one and a half cents. I half expected an unpleasant atmosphere in this dive, but the lack of selfconsciousness was disarming and the music and skill in intricate dances was on a plane of its own.

The faces, the profiles, the grace, the seriousness, and the haunting rhythm of the marimba and drums made the very palms and stars seem natural backdrops in this strangest of places in a strange city. I should like to see what Covarrubias or Diego Rivera would have made of it. (Plate 13.)

If Acapulco had provided us with interesting entertainment of the Earth, earthy, she also held in reserve gifts of the Air and the Sea. When the exciting succession of interests of Wolfgang threatened to slacken, he summoned a friend, who shuttled a six-passenger plane back and forth to Mexico City, doing the eighty miles over and around the great ranges in something less than an hour. Of him, he demanded largesse for us. Asked for my preference, I suggested, with my tongue in my cheek, a low altitude trip northward along the breakers. Knowing that I had flown under many conditions, he looked quickly at me and grinned acquiescence, whereupon I said of course I had been joking, and that, instead, we might do a tourist; climb the mountains and slide down. But he refused to change, and said we would do both.

So, early on the twenty-eighth of November, Jocelyn, Willows and I drove out to the small, fairly flat expanse on the far side of the bay, known by courtesy as the Flying Field. The engine of the little red bus was turning over, and we climbed aboard. It was so narrow that the seats were staggered, and we had access to the windows on both sides. Taxiing to the end of the run we turned and roared over the rubble, lifted, passed over the Miramar, veered north along the shore.

We leveled off at two hundred feet, Fritz sending back his friendly grin, as we both had the same thought.

We slid over the sandy strip between the white, but very low and quiet breakers, and the narrow extent of land bounding the lagoon. The sea was absolutely calm, all but slick, and the fish and the bottom might have been in emerald air. A shark to every hundred yards was the average, some small, some eight feet or more. The slow sinuous winding of the tail and the head of these creatures was most graceful. The speed and the wide angle of vision, fore and aft, through the windows allowed us an unexpected duration of observation of any one object.

The transverse tail flukes were sufficient identification of a pair of dolphins, swimming close together, blowing spray up toward us, and instantly darting frantically away at the sound of our engine. None of the real fish showed any fear of us, our noise or our shadow. A devilfish of unusual size flapped along, and then a school of smaller ones which looked like the reflected shadows of the equally ebony vultures drifting high over our heads. A hammerheaded shark seemed to see us, and turned sideways so that one goggle eye faced straight upward. More devilfish, and then the largest checker-board, eagle ray I ever saw; even its whip tail was visible. Big groupers, almost always in pairs, were close to the breakers, and once a solid school of medium-sized fish swam in a compact circle with a clear center—like an aquatic doughnut. I thought I saw an eel of amazing length, but before it passed from view I resolved it into a long line of unknown fish, swimming head to tail. Twice, flounders of unusual size swam above the bottom, thus becoming visible to us by detaching themselves optically from the sand, by their shadows.

On the landward side, the lagoon passed swiftly, with now and then a house or group of huts on the bank. The red dwelling which came into view was the home of a foreigner who had seven wives and would allow no one to come near his harem. He, and what looked like an infinite brood of offspring, waved cheerily to us as we passed. At the end of the lagoon was an Indian village, and near by, all the egrets in the world rose like a dense snowstorm beneath us, thousands scattering in all directions in stark terror. Pelicans flew steadily and smugly toward us, until they awoke from their nearsighted gaze, or encountered our shadow, or heard the engine, when they bailed overboard and dived apparently quite out of control, barely clearing water or sand.

At last we rose abruptly, gaining welcome altitude in two

great spirals, and I suddenly realized that every muscle ached, held taut throughout the trip. Another grin, very much of relief, for we well knew that this kind of a plane and engine, on this kind of a day, had no business two hundred feet up over thin water and soft sand.

We shut off power, banked steeply and dropped past the Zaca, almost brushing her masts, and then spiraled after the black zopilotes, up and up the first great mountain range. At last, almost touching the bushes, we slid over the knife ridge, and looked straight down into space. Before us lay the old, old road from Acapulco to the City of Mexico, the ancient road of the Conquistadores, the China road, carrying on from the galleons of the Indies. It zigzagged downward, and then stretched out, white and lazy in the day's heat, until it twisted up and over the next Sierra range, and vanished.

Not until we climbed out did Jocelyn have any idea of the rather risky flight we had taken. Fritz said he had often flown over Colima and Popocatepetl when they were in eruption, and on the whole, preferred it to another of our fishing jaunts.

Back on the Zaca, we found her anchored in a tiny bay, the very Puerto del Marques, where, 398 years ago, Cortez built his pitiful little armada of three tiny ships. With two of these, his lieutenant, de Ulloa, explored the Gulf of California (which should be the Gulf of Cortez) and on along the open sea as far north as Cedros Island.[1] The change is very great from the time when the proud galleons of the early Spaniards thronged the waters of Acapulco, laden with the ivory, silks and spices of the Orient.

After dinner we took the launch back to the pier, picked

[1] Zaca Venture, page 6 ff.

up two native canoes and four fishermen, and towed them to the far side of the outer bay. After passing a small gunboat, all lighted up, we were in utter darkness, except for the stars which seemed to be strung on wires just above our heads. The phosphorescence was magnificent. Our wake was a boiling mass of turquoise foam, but an unusual sight was a narrow, intense curved line of pale green, extending out from the side, as if a luminous serpent were gliding with us over the surface of the water.

Finally we came to the end of our launch trip, although how our guide knew was more than I could tell. All I could hear was the swell breaking against some great pile of rocks, seeming to come from all directions at once. I climbed into one of the dugouts and we started off into the utter blackness. The man behind me had a paddle, the blade of which was at least ten inches wide and two feet long, very heavy, and yet he wielded it for hours. The canoe was big and cranky, and exceedingly shallow and, to keep my balance even while sitting, I had to clutch the side with both hands. The man in the bow was reputedly the best fisherman in Acapulco, the very one whose figure adorned the walls of the Mirador bar. He stood up, although the canoe never ceased rolling, and proceeded to light a great torch. This was made of seven-foot splinters of the wood of some special pine, bound together with thongs every six inches. After a match was applied for several minutes it flared up, sputtering smoke and sparks, and continued to burn strongly. Every minute or two it had to be knocked against the boat or struck by a harpoon to get rid of the burned part which fell into the water with much hissing. I found at the end of the evening that my white coat and

94

8. *Chamela Bay.* From the *Zaca* at anchor we can see the dry and arid vegetation which covers the mountains.

trousers were very evenly and thoroughly burned and scorched by the dripping, white-hot resin. With a flat trident on a long, slender pole, a cord attached to his right wrist and the torch in his left hand, the fisher maestro was ready. I found we were after two kinds: one, the gars, called *algujon*, and the other, the gar's cousin, *Ablennes* or snook, locally and appropriately known as *machete*. We spent four hours in this and another distant place, drifting and paddling fast or slow, straight, or gyrating in giddy circles. In this time we speared eight gars and one *machete*.

The size and activity of the fish make this a dangerous sport. Just as the small, jumping halfbeaks are always drawn to our submarine lights, so these great gars are attracted and leap at the torches, and if anyone in the canoe makes a noise or moves, the fish is liable to be distracted and change his direction and strike the person. Men are occasionally killed and one of our fishermen had a terrible scar on his neck where a fish had raked him in mid-air. The fish were not abundant but every now and then we would see a dim form flash by, near the surface. The harpoon would instantly turn in its direction, and the paddler, who apparently never took his eyes from this instrument, at once turned the heavy boat as if it were a birch-bark canoe. Only twice did the thrower miss. Several times we saw monsters which appeared five or six feet long, but those we secured were all about three feet. Once only throughout the whole evening did the man lose his balance. The rest of the time, no matter how we rolled or jerked, his body reacted instantly.

In the course of the evening, the man used up a whole length of torch, and lit a second. After lighting it, he would

95

9. *The Picture Writing Shells of Chamela Bay.* No two of many thousands are alike.

dip all but the burning tip into the water for a minute, to control the spread of the conflagration. We went on, toward the open sea where the swells almost swamped us, and here the fish appeared larger. The two men continued to work together as if it were a millpond. And always the crash of water sounded, close at hand, on an invisible shore.

I have written a few paragraphs of spearing gars at night from a dugout. But I have given no real sense of the mystery of it all. The warm air, the breathlessness, the surrounding walls of solid darkness, the roof of a thousand stars, all shut us in, as if in a closed room. The water seemed a new element, with no sense of wetness; the fish materialized in thin air. One moment a shower of sparks as of falling stars enveloped me, and the next a great silvery fish with double, toothed bayonets thrashed about at my feet. There was no spoken word. The incredible skill of balance, of judgment, of shift to each new tableau, was unreal and hypnotic. It seemed as if it could never cease, and not until we suddenly scraped alongside our launch, and the torch went out with a plop and a sizzle, did I return to reality and know I had passed through a wonderful experience.

CHAPTER IX

THE RIVER OF MUD AND SWEETNESS

ACAPULCO slipped astern; our friends became one with
the crowds on the wharf, houses shrank together, streets
merged, the surrounding, eternal hills lost substance and
joined sea and sky in a blurred cloud on the horizon. We
carried away few scientific specimens from this Mexican city,
but a host of strange memories, written and unwritten, which
will outlast many more concrete things. As the *Zaca* headed
southward we went up in the bow and looked ahead for whatever the sea had next to offer.

A great school of dolphins appeared from nowhere and
acted as escort destroyers to our battleship, but with their
speed and grace they made the *Zaca* a veritable crawling tub.
We recalled a promise made to a distant curator of marine
mammals, hardened our hearts, and bade Pemasa Utu get
one. Looking at the great spindle-shaped creature on deck,
streamlined and finned, it was as difficult as always for me
to visualize a four-footed, furred, terrestrial ancestor of this
mammalian fish. Its scientific destiny was fulfilled to the utmost in the preservation of its black and pied skin, skeleton,
parasites and food.

Old Earth rolled around and sank the Sun in a glory of
gold and red, and early the next morning, coming on deck, I

97

found old Earth still rolling, and bringing up from the sea the selfsame Sun in a reverse but equally breath-taking glory of red and gold. It was the rainless season, but from a black-rimmed cloud, low hung over the distant land, rain was pouring in oblique streaks, like the parallel hair lines on a diffraction grating. My first surprise at this unreasonable sight was changed to a sudden realization that the distant coast of southern Mexico was still rainless. This rainstorm was solely a heavenly affair, the drops, like the sparks from a spent rocket, dying in mid-air, cloud to cloud, watering we knew not what celestial mirage of some invisible skyscape. To the parched land beneath, it was only the momentary shadow of a passing cloud, a swift meteorological sleight-of-hand, a Tantalus-like precipitation and absorption, now you see it, now you don't. And far below, dusty petals crackled, birds panted with parched thirst, and the cacti, watery misers, hugged their humid stores close within their pads.

It was still early on this last day of November when our anchor chain rattled down through eight fathoms. On Toshio's ever-ready lines four catfish came almost as quickly to the surface, up from the bottom, and swung overside, squeaking and protesting after their bewhiskered fashion. Our chart told us that we were at the mouth of an indentation, almost too shallow to be called a bay, into the head of which emptied the Rio Dulce. *Dulce* it might well be, but to the eye it was also *Rio Muy Sucio*, as heralded by the squeaking catfish. It seemed to promise poor hunting for our mental fish larder, but ere this we had plucked plums—or is it figs—from apparent thistles, and the most bromidic mind knows that lilies spring from no more promising mud than that which stained

98

the sea about us with deltoid fans of opacity. So we took the otter boat and the pram and started hopefully for the River of Sweetness.

From a collection of miserable thatched huts huddled behind a mud bar at the mouth of the stream, there came forth a jefe of sorts in a dugout. The crew seemed to be working in shifts, some pulling ragged strokes with oars of assorted lengths, and an equal number bailing with more energy than is usually manifested by Mexican peons. Documents were demanded of us, but without much conviction or desire. We compromised amicably with several dozen cigarettes, their tissue paper envelopes apparently more acceptable than any Letters of Marque we might proffer. We also saved the rowers from imminent drowning by towing them back to the village.

As we chugged up river, fish came occasionally to the surface with a glance in our direction which might have been interpreted as begging us to remove them from their suffocating environment. We would have been glad to comply but the absolute turbidity, combined with the exceedingly swift current, enforced a total ignorance of the ichthyological content which, I fear, will still be unbroken on the day of our death.

We looked about us with envy. We were merely Lords of Creation going against the current in a complex launch, while all about us were Better Fishers than we were, Gunga Din. We watched snakebirds submerge quietly and come up with a fish speared through and through by both mandibles; we saw gannets plummet, guided by some sort of magical mud vision, and emerge with mullet-like prey held pincer-wise. And finally, like the helpless humans which we were, we coveted the automatic casting of the pelican's trap. He lifted his head, his beak positively drooling small fry, and we could not even perch on his back, like the small gulls, and snatch the scaly crumbs which fell from the great bird's beak.

However, being at heart that thing barely tolerated by Ultimate Scientists—a Naturalist—my allegiance, impelled by environmental sour grapes, turned from Saint Walton to Saint Audubon, and in the twinkling of an eye my mind's interest, accelerating past evolutions, shifted from fish to birds. With unichthyological facility, I unlimbered my glasses and reveled in the flocks which rose from water, bank and trees as we went on up the stream, now become *el Rio de Pájaros*.

Having been an ornithologist most of my life, the mental observing and recording of every flying thing long since passed the conscious stage, and joined the pleasant group of involuntary actions, together with winking and breathing. In order that a book such as this may inspire a voluntary desire of ownership on the part of something more than a dozen readers, I suppress my instinctive wish to include every such list of birds. But the avian fauna of the Rio Dulce was really exceptional, and representative of many other favoured places along this west coast, so I yield to my craving. As the sodden dope fiend reaches with trembling hand for just one more sniff of "snow," so I use this excuse for one grand list of birds, and right in the text too.

An intensification of tropicalness was apparent in this place, and there was just enough of open water, swamps and shrubs, with alternating clumps of high, dry cactus areas and lower almost-forest, to attract and sustain a large number of birds.

For the first time on this trip we saw brilliant colour in

large masses, rafts of floating water hyacinths dappled with purple and gold standards, and trees of solid yellow bloom. A good omen was a freshly emerged *Junonia coenia*, or some unimportant subspecies, waving its wings from a hyacinth leaf. In varying sizes and degrees of paleness and intensity of colour and pattern this delightful little butterfly has waited for my coming in all parts of the world. In my boyhood New England I made its acquaintance, and it was Number 3 in my very first collection. I knew it and know it as *Junonia coenia*. With utter and happy disregard for specificity or newly unearthed generic names, regardless of subspecies, forms, varieties and aberrations, I always whisper or scream or think *Junonia coenia* when and wherever it again comes into view. In Bermuda it is small and keeps to the ground and low shrubs out of the force of the wind; in the Himalayas it is also small but, like the flowers of those lofty heights, unusually brilliant in colour.

Returning to our Rio Dulce, besides the deltic village, there was a scattering of huts and dilapidated casas along the banks. But, as elsewhere, this was a land of poverty-stricken peons. Caballeros carry a well-sharpened machete and a revolver or two, and are draped with pounds upon pounds of cartridges, in belts, both horizontal and oblique, all ready, if need be, to decimate their fellows. But none here could afford shotguns or shells, and fish hatcheries were unheard-of, so no excuse offered for the slaughter of fish-eating birds as in more civilized countries.

In my flaunted bird list I give only common names, for except in a few instances the species are self-evident at first glance of the birdinthebush.

To remove the curse from an unadorned bird list I want
to look at the feathered natives of Rio Dulce first as essen-
tially waterbirds, and second, as doing their fishing in inter-
estingly individual ways. If half a hundred men should start
fishing with hand lines and worms in this river, they would
doubtless catch a good lot of a few kinds, but when these
became rare or wary, the fishermen would starve. Along comes
a man with a casting net, or a dry fly, or a spoon or a baited
wire trap, and each becomes at once eminently successful. If
all the handliners starved to death except a handful, then they
and all the others would continue to make a good living. Then
a sneak thief would creep along the bank and snitch fish
from the creels and he would prosper in his way. This apparently silly parable becomes stark reality when we apply it to
the fishing birds of this little river.

The fishers we saw at the entrance, both before and after
crossing the bar, seemed to put a maximum of energy and
pep into their methods. In a scant three feet of water, two
bombs dropped close alongside the boat. They were duds as
far as bombs were concerned, but in both cases a big, brown
booby emerged with a shining fish in its beak. It laboured up
and off, and while still dripping salt water gave itself a sudden
twist, oriented the fish, and let it slide into its final resting
place. That was the end of that, we thought; but no, one
of the birds hurtled back upon its trail, and shot past us
again, horizontally this time, with a great, bent-winged man-
o'-war bird in terrific but effortless pursuit. Twice the booby
dodged and doubled, but it was like trying to escape one's
shadow. Finally it tried altitude, but this was fatal, and the
frigatebird seemed to shake gravitation from its wings and

fairly fall upwards. Just as it soared, ready to drop on its victim, the harassed booby surrendered. The fish which we thought had passed forever from sight, appeared again, apparently as good as ever, and did a nose dive which no flyingfish could imitate. A zigzag streak of sable lightning followed, picked the fish delicately from mid-air only a few feet above the surface, daintily swallowed it and scooped up a chaser of salt water. In the distance the lightened booby disappeared in high gear, mad and hungry if ever any bird was. A feathered harpoon and a high-air robber had performed the prelude to our anglers' sonata. Rio Dulce's bar blazed with emotion; we were vitally interested and excited, the booby was disconsolate, the frigatebird was triumphant, and the fish—well, he probably thought no more about it. As Bret Harte has said, "The subsequent proceedings interested him no more." In human ethics the booby was an honest toiler, the frigatebird a reprehensible robber. But who are we to pass judgment outside our own field of action? Like the fish, who are we to worry?

It was not until we were coming out of the river later in the day that we saw a replica of the robber incident but one which, to the spectator, was leavened with humour and devoid of rancor. A flock of brown pelicans were using their pouches and themselves as living cast nets, and making fine hauls of silver fry just inside the bar. With them was a quartet of laughing gulls packing themselves full of the dribbling fish. Again and again they would perch on the backs or tops of the heads of the pelicans and seize every stray fishlet as it trickled out of the corners of the draining beak. We could actually see the great birds looking down their noses at their diminutive, impudent, gate-crashing, penny-snatchers, but they were helpless to resent anything until they had swallowed their enormous mouthful. There seemed, indeed, no especial ill-will on the part of the pelicans.

Even my Puritan ancestors would have been hard put to it to include the gulls and the frigatebirds in the same hand- or wing-cuffed category of evil doers, and being safely separated from my first American ancestor by more than two hundred and ninety years and ten generations, I blatantly classed the acts of both birds as "bright and beautiful sin." In fact, I rather faintly damned the two fishers of the first part with the comforting dictum of Oscar Wilde, "There is no sin but stupidity."

Several flocks of terns, the smallest of all their kind, flew neatly in and out of the river, now and then imitating the method of the boobies, but more exquisitely and deftly, as a rapier to a broadsword.

Up river we came to the first of the true anglers. Knee-deep across the river, or what in a heron is heel-deep, in the muddy water, was a pair of great blues. Always remember, I am speaking of species, not subspecies. By the slaughter of one of these splendid birds I could have called it with taxonomic precision *lessonii, wardi, treganzai, fannini* or *sancti-lucae*. At fifty yards they were great, they were bluish and in general inseparable from my boyhood's friends, so I was content. On this particular river trip *Ardea herodias* was good enough for me and I am sure the patient herons shared my humour. Throughout all the time of passing I could not detect even the rolling of an eyeball, but before we disappeared one bird took four steps and stabbed. I could see no result but a muddy splash.

The heron family now appeared en masse, but we must think of them first as fishers. Our Samoans could slip overboard and bring up a live fish from the bottom, or a great basking turtle in their bare hands. In this they were like the booby or tern in using their entire body. The herons introduce the angler's methods; like a human fisherman in rubber boots, manipulating a rod and reel with hands alone, these birds use only their beak and neck. In the course of the river we saw nine species of herons, making ten altogether. There were snowy and American egrets, little blue herons, little greens and Louisianas, bitterns, black- and yellow-crowned night herons and boat-bills. The world's record for patient immobility must be given to the big egrets and the bittern. They can out-Simeon Stylites and on a much smaller stance. In clear water they can at least see the approach of a prospective fish, but in the Rio Dulce the chances were infinitely against a fish breaking mud exactly at the spot where they were focused. Spearing fish through a small hole in the ice is my only adequate simile. I always have the feeling that a heron is posing for my special benefit and that after I leave he does plenty of hustling about.

The smaller herons—snowy egrets, little blues and greens and Louisianas—are compressed to emaciation, and head on, to a fish, must look like amorphous, coloured cardboard. A correlation of this invisibility is less need for immobility, and we find the smaller birds stepping slowly and highly in a search for food. The little greens, whether along our mill-ponds or in this tropical setting, have a procedure all their own. They have discarded patience for pursuit, and creep along the low branches of the mangroves or the shallows, and have even adopted the teetering or tail-tipping of rails, sand-pipers and water thrushes—a habit so unique that if classification were based on physical activities, little green herons would be removed quite out of their family and put into that of the rails. I have spoken of coloured cardboard, and the edibility of this substance might be that of herons themselves for all the worry they give to predators. Some are white; others, green, blue or rufous; little blues are white in their youth, particoloured in adolescence and solid blue when grown up. I must say that if I were a hawk, the sight of the strong, sharp beak, the clutching feet and toes, and the thought of the scant coating of dry flesh on the bones of a heron would all help to ensure their immunity to attack.

Just as we humans go jack-lighting for fish at night, we saw from time to time, on this river, the big-eyed night herons waiting among the foliage for the dusk. With them was that absurd tropical cousin, the boat-billed, with the beak of the other birds enlarged, rounded, made into a tiny model of the pelican-idea.

Other birds began where the herons left off and brought to bear such ingenious instruments of prehension that it is a wonder the fish and worms do not vanish from the world. The ibises—white, scarlet and glossy—probed the mud with their sensitive, curved forceps, and the lovely roseate spoon-bills sifted out unfortunate fish and other mud-dwellers with sidewise swathes of their flat mandibles. The wood ibis—or, better, stork—was the dumbest-looking and the cleverest of all. He stood in the shallows, reached out one great foot and with his toes carefully stirred up the mud and water, with beak poised ready to seize whatever attempted to escape. Cormorants often swim a few strokes under water after their prey, but if I were a fish I would dread the snakebird more than any other enemy. They seemed as much fish as fowl, they submerged so easily, and in addition to this facility they were fast swimmers and kept their beak closed. This latter habit meant that a single, quick, piercing stab was all that was needed.

Other fish-eaters there were, but by accident, not by nature. These were the vultures—red-headed and black—which welcomed any stranded, ancient, dead fish, while even the small hawks, kiskadees and grackles dipped down and picked up floating fry. Four ospreys passed over but none dived. To these we give the anglers' banzai. No robbers or parasites they, but hunters with sufficient skill to dive, to snatch and to rise, from air to water, to air again, lacking webs, clad in land birds' plumage, and making their capture with talons and toes alone.

I have not included the curlew, the willets, stilts and sandpipers, for they are rather worm-chasers, and to catch a worm they, as we, simply go after it and dig. Doves, parrots, cuckoos, flycatchers, orioles, martins and warblers—these filled the trees and the air with color or with song, but all their thoughts were on food far other than the dull-scaled inhabitants of the muddy current.

Next morning, heading ever southward, we realized how well protected this whole coast is, against the intrusion of small vessels, and especially sailing ships. One of the most dangerous obstacles is man-made. A large steamer, the *San Francisco*, was wrecked here not many years ago, just south of the Rio Dulce, and the currents and general configuration of the coast resulted in a rapid and extensive silting up to within six or eight feet of the surface, so that today we find the great Tartar Shoals, seething with breakers, reaching out farther and farther for more prey to add to the submerged steamer nucleus which, like a pearl in an oyster, lies hidden in their heart.

Also, from here southward, for some hundreds of miles, vessels may suddenly, without warning, experience the terrible Tehuantepeckers. These are storms, northers, apparently connected in some way with the flattish, narrow Atlantic-Pacifico isthmus at this point. A calm sea and a breathless air may turn, in less than half an hour, into a gale with cross seas fatal for any small boat. A Tehuantepecker feels otherwise toward very tiny, soft-winged moths, for after such a smashing storm, three of these, gray and mottled like fluttering bits of tweed, came straight out of the smother to our deck lamp, and there promptly expired from the heat. To avoid these unheralded hurricanes, it is necessary for ships such as the Zaca to hug the shore closely, thereby inviting destruction from the shoals. The alternative is to set the course fifty or more miles out to sea.

CHAPTER X

TWO BAYS OF PURGATORY

ON Thursday, the second day of December, the weather looking propitious (as Columbus might have said) we sped southward full speed. But the Evil Genius of Meteorology looked down, grinned at our hopefulness, and beckoned. Off came the Tehuantepecker and all day we rolled and pitched miserably. Work was impossible. We could only hold fast to anything within reach, lie impotently gazing at the active ceiling, or crawl futilely about, picking up a book and putting it down again. Under such circumstances it is always profitable to marvel at the unbelievable activity of the Inorganic World —air, wind, water.

In late afternoon we were hurtled into a little bay, the Tehuantepecker dying away a few minutes after we were out of its reach. Doubtless in our present mental state, the Coast of Dis would have seemed a fair haven, but in the failing light the scene around us really seemed a very lovely place.

In this joyful aftermath of relaxation I got me an atlas and a chart and the three of us went into a private conference. I found that twenty-two hundred and fifty miles west of the West Indian island of Dominica, on the Pacific coast of Mexico, is a series of three semi-connected bays which go by the grand names of Guatulco, Santa Cruz and Tangola-Tangola. They are so small that on any moderately sized map of

Mexico they are not accorded the honour of the slightest tremor on the coast line. Even on the highest-powered chart, their names extend clear across their respective bays. So, on this December afternoon, we sailed into the northernmost of the trio, Guatulco. It was so diminutive that when halfway to the head, the Zaca had to be kedge-anchored, fore and aft, to keep her from swinging too near the shore. Hardly had we passed the outermost headland with our Tehuantepecker howling derisively astern, when a ten-foot devilfish flew past us and rubbed against our bow as it went.

Early next morning we went to the head of the bay and landed through three slow, friendly breakers, which washed us high up on the beach and jettisoned us gently on the sand. As I stepped out, I saw at my feet a great bivalve absurdly like our boat, which also had been deposited without harm on this sandy slope. Three Mexicans appeared from a cluster of ramshackle huts and began to tie up great bundles of recently dried garfish. The fish were quite complete, with heads, tails and odds and ends of entrails, and in addition to recently dried, I should have added half dried. They smelled to high heaven, yet the fishermen said they were headed inland to sell them. I wanted to ask many questions about this place but the trio seemed in an urgent hurry, and shouldering, or, rather, heading their odoriferous luggage they set out, with an audible trail of humming flies following eagerly in their wake.

We walked about for a while, and suddenly became aware of the reason for the haste of the Mexicans. The beach as we saw it in early morning was as lovely as any idealized tropical shore; there were graceful flowering trees on low, overhanging cliffs, dropping their petals actually into the water of the sea;

10. *The Bay of Manzanillo.* Tens of thousands of moonfish circle our submerged light, anti-clock-wise.

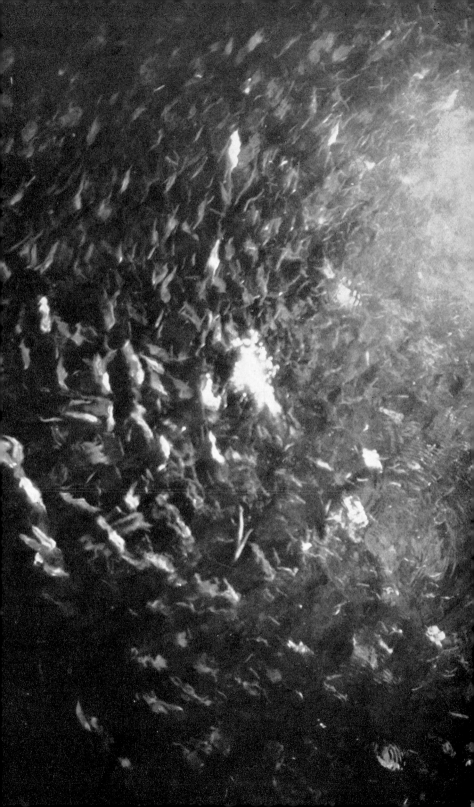

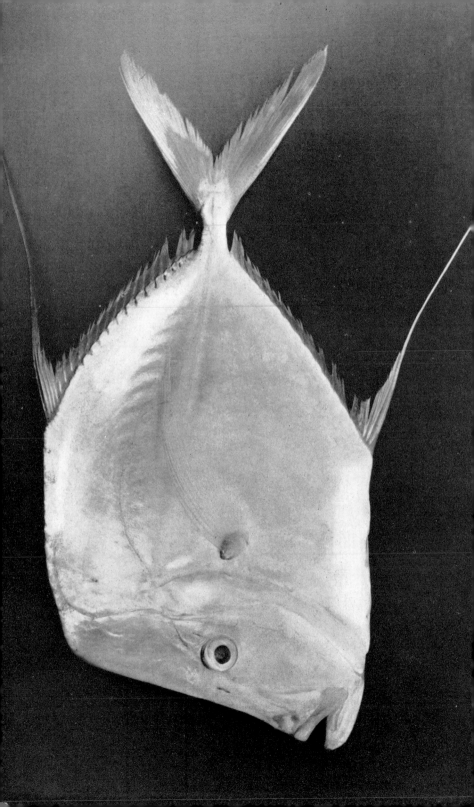

the sand was soft and of the whitest, the sky was a perfect blue, the air moved slowly in a gentle, soothing breeze. As I looked around, the whole world seemed a place of peace and delight. Well separated, we were walking slowly along the curve of sand, when I suddenly saw my distant companions acting strangely. Two leaned over and slapped themselves in a sort of rhythmic dance; another ran swiftly up into the scrub, while a fourth dashed into the low breakers, shorts and all. Insanity seemed suddenly to have attacked the Zaca's staff. Then my bare legs began to tingle, and sudden sharp pricks were felt. I looked down and saw the air, for two feet above the sand, foggy with uncountable midges or sandflies. Call them what you will, we christened them with a whole new series of good Anglo-Saxon titles, doubtless merely adding to an already ample synonymy of extant Spanish *epítetos*.

I chose the scrub for sanctuary, and a dozen yards inland I left behind every member of the swarm. Their zone of influence was as circumscribed as their bodies were minute. As I skirted the beach beyond the reach of the organic flames, I saw, of course, things of beauty and interest—new shells, stranded, bleached skeletons of rare fish lying on the sand. At one place I ventured down. It did not seem possible that the apparently clear air, the uninhabited sand could harbor such agony. As I fled it was like running the gauntlet in old days of Indian torture, and the delighted whoops of my heartless friends enhanced the simile.

I caught hundreds of the insects in a single swoop of the net, and although most of them passed easily through the mesh, I bottled several and examined them on board.

Their eyes were iridescent emerald, thorax of oxidized

111

11. *Moonfish from the Night Light Horde.* They are thin as paper, silvery as tinsel, and are first cousins to jacks and pompanos.

bronze, abdomen of glowing amber, legs golden, shading into dark on thighs and feet, eight-jointed antennae coppery gold, and wings large and perfectly hyaline. In length they stretched 1.5 mm. or sixteen to the inch. They possessed a short, innocent-looking beak, but it was a weapon which drove us frantic from the beaches, morning and evening, and our wounds required constant attention to avoid serious infection, to say nothing of sleepless nights. No wonder the Mexicans have established their town of Guatulco miles inland, away from the bay.

Mosquitoes seemed quite absent, but during the day the swarms of Simulidae or sandflies made two beach trips all that we could tolerate. After our first day at Guatulco we were finely pitted with blood specks and the swelling and itching became almost unbearable. The red-bugs were bad in the shrub, but as usual I became gradually immune to them. Ticks also were present and added their enthusiastic attentions to our poor bodies, although taken alone they would not have been a factor in the general unpleasantness. If we found a ready-made trail, all discomforts were non-existent, but the moment we were tempted to turn aside, to push through the undergrowth, trouble started. The botanical barriers were much worse than in any more northern desert. The candelabra cacti grew straight up and were walked around easily, but the ground for miles inland was covered with masses of half dead, fallen clusters of spines from the palmate types which here seemed to be almost creeping, and often hid the ground from view. Acacias with their varied assortment of spines blocked the edges of the cattle and burro trails, with such variations toward exquisite torture as the bull's-horn species, whose spines held you tightly, the while from their hollows, legions of stinging ants poured forth their formic acid and completed the purgatorial round. The second day at Guatulco I set this combination of vegetable and animal blitzkrieg into action when I attempted to go about twenty feet in an untrailed direction. I saw some birds on a flowering tree, but I never reached the tree.

The coast of this part of southern Mexico is really set apart, a halfway place of no definite classification, not wholly desert and far from qualifying as fertile tropical, yet with features of each in their most unpleasant aspects. It had a real interest because of the actual uncertainty of its facies, but it was heavily defended from patient, prolonged scrutiny by most adequate barriers, as far as man was concerned.

When we were driven from the scrub by static obstacles, and from the beach by exceedingly active ones, we recalled to one another that, after all, our expedition was supposed to be a marine one, and took to the water.

Guatulco proved an unsatisfactory place, because our captures were so sporadic and uncertain. Three hours of hard work with seine, bang-bang or helmet might yield almost nothing of particular value, and then some delectable specimen would fairly swim into net or jar, and force its capture upon us. The water of this bay was exceedingly cold and made our helmet dives short and chilly. We tried out wire fish traps for the first time in the Pacific, variously baited, and with good success. But here, too, luck occasionally failed us, for a trap left overnight would sometimes contain nothing but a great, mud-colored moray eel of Falstaffian proportions. The second time this happened I became suspicious and dissected him. In his capacious stomach I found not only all of our bait but the distinctly recognizable remains of ten fish, any one of which unswallowed, would have been a prize. After that red-riding-hood experience, we pulled our traps up at shorter intervals. (Plate 16.)

One of the small beachlets of Guatulco had a real coral reef, the first we had seen deserving of the name, some distance off shore. It was roughly about fifty by two hundred yards, and some thirty from the beach. Like the semi-desert landscape, it was not a pukka coral reef in the tropical sense of the word, the heads being low and the branches brown, two to six inches in length, and crowded close together. Small serranids and eels loved it and many other fish which fled at the first hint of disturbance. We sent the boats and the huskier members of the crew to the reef, with orders to bring as much as possible of it back. By pushing pails and tubs beneath the heads, they were pried off and lifted on board with a minimum loss of the inhabitants. The northern character was still apparent in the make-up of animal life, and many groups, such as serpent-stars, worms and mollusks which, in a tropical reef should have been present in great numbers and brilliancy, were scarce.

On the deck we squatted Hindu-wise, and with hammer and chisel attacked the unlovely masses of coral. Baby rock-fish and demoiselles, and strange slippery brotulids slithered out, while small sea-cucumbers twisted about in the low-geared activity which Nature has vouchsafed them.

The dominant tenants were small red crabs and equally diminutive snapping shrimps. Wholly unlike one another in general shape, they yet were absurdly similar in colour and

114

pattern and certain reactions. They varied from a rich ferruginous red to a dark pink, and when seen deep within the interstices of the branches they appeared identical. The tips of the big claws were black. Both became terribly excited at being chivied about their erstwhile quiet domicile, and at the first hint of trouble all slid down into the deepest crevices of the coral, like firemen sliding down their pole on a sudden alarm. The crabs and shrimps were both suited perfectly to this performance, but spatially speaking, in diametrically opposite ways. The crabs were excessively *flattened*, thus enabling them to go sideways down a crack of smallest caliber, while the shrimps were correspondingly *compressed*, both body and claw, so that they followed the crabs, but tail first, around the close, irregular coral columns and stairways. If by chance they reached a cul-de-sac together, a fight promptly ensued, each apparently blaming the other for all this unprecedented upheaval of their cosmos. If epithets flew, the shrimps would certainly be saying, "You miserable blighters, you *Trapezia cymodoce ferruginea!*" And the crabs must of necessity answer, "Same to you, you sons of *Crangon ventrosus*, you!"

As a matter of fact, lacking vocal ejaculations, the shrimps can still express their emotions aloud, and as their homes are invaded, a veritable crescendo of castanets, of sharp snaps and clicks would arise, near and far, as they frantically snapped their chelae in horror or in despair.

When I had broken through to their last retreat, with backs against the marble wall this thin red line of brave little crustaceans surrendered first their huge, black-tipped claws, one after another. The shrimps then let go, and hurled themselves down to whatever lay below. If this happened to be the water in the tub, they swam swiftly away, but if they fell on deck they lay helpless on the flat, dry surface, faintly clicking their requiem.

The crabs, on the contrary, when exposed beyond peradventure of further concealment, clung like grim death with all eight legs, fencing the approaching forceps with wildly waving claws, holding on even after these had been sacrificed. If they fell on deck, they scurried like mad for the scuppers, and flung themselves over side. This probably was a fatal act, with only the result, of problematical satisfaction to them, of expiring in their native element. The chance of a morsel of such conspicuous edibility running the vertical gauntlet of all the voracious fish beneath our keel, before reaching safety within another coral reef, was indeed slender.

Our chart—testament, guide, friend, hope—showed that at Guatulco we were in the first of three baylets, so after another skirmish with sandflies which turned at once into a rout for us, we circled the next outjutting point of land and entered the haven of Santa Cruz Bay. But the governing noun was a misnomer, and the chart was wrong or the bay had shifted, for there was no protection from the sheer Pacific. Nevertheless we allowed ourselves to be washed ashore on the great, lazy swells.

A single hut with overturned dugout and cracked paddles marked where a Mexican family—apparently the First F., the Last F. and the Only Family of Santa Cruz—had fled either from sandflies or to some Guatulcan fiesta. A dark spot far down the beach resolved through the binoculars into a forlorn, emaciated dog, seated on the sand, gazing miserably out to sea, and now and then raising its muzzle to high heaven and howling with prolonged but absolutely silent emotion.

Passing an enormous, weed-hung rock well out from the shore, we followed an impulse and flopped overboard for a swim. The swells lulled us, gently lifting and lowering our floating selves. Then I thought, for no reason at all, that I would seize the right moment, let my feet reach the side of the rock and kick myself far out. Just as I paddled myself into position, the mother of all swells came along, swung me up to the level of the very summit, and then sucked me down, down, exposing a great, solid, horrid zone of long-spined sea-urchins. Against these, except for the sudden exposure, I should have joyfully kicked and been laid up for weeks unknown. This was about enough, and we all scrambled and fell over the gunwales and shouted the nautical equivalent of "Home James!"

But Santa Cruz had one more ace up her sleeve. Word had gone overland from Guatulco that the owner and staff on the Zaca were toothsome morsels, and off on the gentle evening breeze, together with the faint scent of acacias, came patrolling squadrons of sandflies. We could neither see nor hear them, but the sense of feeling was still strong in spite of our Guatulco battle scars.

Whenever I desire to conjure up a picture of supreme dismalness, I recall the scene of a deserted dog, seated in the exact center of a waste of sand, howling silently to itself and to the sea, on a lonely beach of Santa Cruz.

CHAPTER XI

TANGOLA-TANGOLA

ON the eighth of December, soon after the sandflies had turned themselves into sea-going, machine-gunning planes, we organized a scouting expedition to the third and last of the trio of baylets—Tangola-Tangola—and found that it also differed widely from the chart, but in all the right ways. Also we liked its name; it had the stuttering suggestion of a South Sea Island. So we shook the last drops of Santa Cruz water from our propeller and swung to anchor in this new bay.

Tangola-Tangola may be taken as typical of the bays in this section of southernmost Mexico, a sort of no-man's land as to north and south. Our first impressions, as we scouted along shore or walked on land, may be the best.

Back from the crescent of the water's edge the shore rises into low hills covered thickly with scrubby growth or small trees, partly dry, partly green, with here and there masses of white, or scattered blossoms of bright yellow. The less dense white blooms are our old friends the temple flowers or frangi-panni. It is interesting that this is the original home of the white variety, now so widely grown over the world. The solid masses of white blossoms make us think of snow, and like that substance these alter and sometimes disappear in the course of a day. They are not what they appear to be—tree blossoms—but are purple-hearted, white convolvulus or morning-glories, which, liana-like, climb to the summit of these trees and there cover every branch with their delicate pigments.

The only radical departure from this type of foliage is the low stretches of intense green mangroves, marking the contours of lagoons of various sizes just back of the sand dunes.

We spent five days at Tangola-Tangola and most of the time I explored strange environments, observing and collecting, but not settling down to study any one place or group of creatures or individuals. So I propose for the first and last time to "do" Tangola[2], much as a Baedeker tourist would do a cathedral town. The emphasis will be on the general and the obvious, as when I list the varied environments which I investigated for their animal life.

For example, after landing through the surf, we rushed up the beach out of the reach of the following wave, and the sandflies; we kept right on to the top of the beach, where the life of the dry land began. There we saw the inevitable mangrove lagoon fed by some indistinct sluggish stream. A trail led off to one side which, we discovered, could be followed for miles without getting anywhere. Now and then we looked up to high heaven and discovered a wholly unexpected zone of life; we returned to the sandy shore and explored the caves and tidepools; we seined the shallow water neck-deep along the beach; we watched our motorboats shuttle back and forth with trolling lines out, and set, expectant expressions on the faces of the fishermen; we lowered wire traps, temptingly baited, in likely places; we exploded sticks of dynamite in spots difficult of access; we drew series of small dredges in shallow water, in a line from shore to yacht, as a trapper runs his line of traps; we donned helmet and walked about, thirty to forty feet down on the bottom; from the Zaca hand-line fishing went on steadily; after dark the night light worked its magic; and when at last we left any particular bay we drew nets and dredges down to the cold, black depths a half mile from the surface. Thus we strove to search out every part of every bay, learning what facts we might and gathering all the specimens humanly possible: This is the syllabus of our endeavours!

Landing through breakers is always exciting. When there were several of us the danger, even from an unexpected undertow, was reduced to minimum, yet we were always worried about guns, cameras and glasses until we were safe ashore. Curiously enough, the greatest risk in this respect, until we learned how to cope with it, was after the boat had stranded in barely six inches of water.

With our precious instruments clutched tight, we sat braced on the seats, facing shoreward while our Samoan maneuvered so that we should start in on the summit of one of the lesser swells, and ride it swiftly, with the next, perhaps a giant, following close behind. I have never seen any explanation, and it is probably an endless series of coincidences, but time after time, the waves seemed to come in threes—three ordinary ones, then a whale of a fourth. Up and down we would float, high aloft and down into the trough of swell after swell. Then Pe's muscles would ripple; quick, powerful strokes gave us impetus, so that we remained on the crest, rushing along with it, faster and faster, yet holding back so as to be just on the forward shoulder of the green-curving breaker; then a final rush through the seething, white smother.

The froth came past, far higher than our gunwale, but water at such a moment has no time to turn and pour sideways, and it and we must hurtle shorewards. With a final pull, Pe shouted to us to leap. Even as we obeyed, the sand had stopped the boiling flood and turned it back.

Now was the critical moment, and we had learned to look at the boat or at the shore, but never at the water around us. If we did this last, the optical illusion would be our undoing. Time after time, until I had learned better, I stepped out of an absolutely stationary boat, solidly grounded in the sand, and pitched forward headlong on my face. The stop had occurred without a jolt, but the return wave, rushing past us out to sea, gave the impression that we were surging swiftly ahead. All our instinctive sense of balance came into play to counteract this apparent movement, and before our feet could undeceive us, could tell that there was no motion whatever, we would crash to our knees in the sandy rush. It was the old story of another train slowly passing our stationary one, only this was deception carried to the Nth power. The best way of all was to shut one's eyes and jump.

Just as we started swell-riding in Tangola-Tangola, a terrific tug on my fishing line nearly upset me, and some great fish splashed astern. Simultaneously, a magnificent male man-o'-war bird swooped on narrow, angular wings, its toy balloon of a scarlet throat pouch half inflated, and looked at my catch. I had only a net and the line in my hand, and when we stranded I was over like a flash. All I had learned about not looking at the passing water was forgotten in the excitement, and although we were motionless in three inches of water I shot

121

forward in a beautiful somersault. My wrist was cut deep by the taut line before I could get up, stop the fish, avoid the next wave and haul in a lovely lilac and bronze jack-crevelly, fighting to the last, and drawing several others of his kind up to the curving, transparent mirror of the second line of swells.

If Tangola-Tangola be considered as one of a triple line of bays, then within its own confines we must count still lesser baylets, and these also in threes. Each was separated by small, rocky promontories, like diminutive Frailes. These great crags of handsome cream and white granite, speckled with black, were cut into the shapes of all sorts of animals and monuments, smooth and rounded as if polished by some mysterious tropical glacier, yet all undetached, superlative cameos and intaglios.

Next to the animal and plant life on a small, circumscribed island, which is the most fascinating study in the world, is the relation between the brink of the sea and the land, the tidal zone where air and water fight eternally for dominance. Here at one side of the bay were steep cliffs. The crumbs of seeds fallen from vegetation high overhead, which had dropped or been blown over, had mostly succumbed to death by salt water. But a few had clutched crevices with outstretched hooks or feather-light wings and found meager life in accumulated dust. Here were orphans of the desert, overlooking the unending waters of the sea; weakling pads of cactus with upraised palms begging for only a very, very little moisture without salt to carry on their futile vitality in a crack of the rock; even a diminutive candelabrum cactus, holding itself very straight like its parents on the desert which it had never seen. A tiny acacia with two fragile leaves and a single golden blossom, as brave as if it were the first, and not the last of its individual line. For a moment I was threatened with a spate of sentimental comparison with human beings, so many of us who are on the brink of—but I refrained, and walked to the nearest tide-pool. I saw a stone lying loosely at the edge and strained to turn it over, but soon realized that I was trying to shift Mexico and the Sierra del Sur themselves.

Although sunflower starfish are common all along this western coast, my eyes, more familiar with the shallows of New Jersey and Bermuda, were always surprised to see the well-known five-rayed contour increased to thirty and forty. Recalling that somewhere I had read that these many-armed stars have been known to measure four feet across, I was always on the lookout for one of these exciting, giant sunbursts.

Our doctor, Liljencrantz, begged for some kind of a scientific job, so I set him at work making a graph of the relative arm numbers of thirty of these starfish. He assembled his material into a single pool and solemnly began his count. Soon he handed me the following very satisfactory list:

1	star had	28	arms
1		32	
4		33	
3		34	
6		35	
5		36	
4		37	
3		38	
2		39	
1		40	

Hopefully he totted up and then asked, "Why are there more sunstars with 35 arms, and why are there none with 27 and with 41 arms?"

And I brightly and promptly answered, "I haven't the foggiest idea." And thus ended the doctor's first scientific lesson on Tangola-Tangola!

On the rocks at the east end of the bay which I visited on the twelfth of December, giant limpets were everywhere, especially on the outermost promontories. They were really big shells, measuring about four by six inches, sloping up at a slow, comfortable angle to a blunt summit. Hardly a trace of the original surface was ever visible, the roof being covered with a thatch of algae, barnacles, moss animals and a regular zoo of small, active beings. At almost low tide, as far down as I could see, the limpets were crawling about. Above water they were scattered quite regularly in general abundance but with no regularity as to orientation of head, rear or side, averaging about two limpet lengths from each other. This made it difficult for any individual to move in a straight line without touching or climbing over the shell of a neighbor. Long before the tide covered them, the limpets began to stand on tiptoe, which is to say about a half inch from the rock, to get under way and to graze. Each was surrounded by an aura of short, greenish algae. (Plate 15.)

I selected one limpet, named him Breathless, and watched him. He protruded his head and began creeping slowly forward. As he moved he exposed the surface of the rock where he had been resting, and I saw that in this as in the others, there was a deposit, thin and white, of lime where the body and edge of the shell had lain. The head of my limpet was bent down and the tips of the black horns or tentacles were touching the surface, playing deliberately about as he went, evidently feeling out the way. The mouth was constantly applied to the rock. Wherever this passed, a narrow swath of algae was eliminated, the rock being quite clearly visible, and not hidden as before the passing of the snail's scythe. Soon the limpet came in contact with his nearest neighbor and kept on pushing. The animal pushed against raised its shell and partly turned, facing the intruder, pushing beneath the other's shell. It was a struggle between living tanks. I could detect the strain and apparent leverage. This continued for several minutes, every down-crashing rain of spray from the advancing waves giving them increased energy. For a time the push was equal, resulting only in both shells being slightly canted upward, then my friend gave way and turned to one side. All this time he had never ceased grazing from his neighbor's land. My last view of Breathless showed him turned, headed for the pasturage of another of his fellows. As he sped, his neck (if such a term can be used) behind the head was lifted clear of the rock, arched upward so that only the mouth, the tentacle tips and the oval foot touched the surface.

On many of the limpets large barnacles were growing, and whenever a wave covered the mollusk even for a few seconds, the crustaceans opened their ivory gates and swept madly at the water with their little curved feet. On two large adjoining rocks covered with about two hundred of the great shells, every limpet had a small limpet attached to its shell. A few had as many as three. As the greater one crawled slowly from its form, the young one on its back, at the same time, also left its pitch, its camping place showing a white tissue of lime.

Within ten minutes, while I watched, one small limpet made a complete circuit of the shell of its mount, eating as it went. Fascinated, I examined several small ones with a hand lens to see if by chance I could detect a third generation upon *their* shells, but nothing was visible but minute crustaceans, sow-bug cousins of the sea.

The colour of the animals themselves was uniform, the head and tentacles black, while the foot which projected behind as the creature progressed was liver-coloured, mottled with black. The problem of nourishment was an interesting one. It would almost seem that the growth of the algal food must keep pace with the garnered harvest of each day's requirements. There is not the slightest doubt that each limpet lived in its own form perhaps for years, but whether it was able to trek past all its neighbours and go on prolonged foraging expeditions I cannot tell. Somehow it must be able to find sufficient aliment to return to its own particular home between tides.

This apparent homing was too important to accept without definite proof and finally I located two forms which were abnormal. At one point in the circumference of each there was an irregularity. I began searching and soon found both tenants. I pried them from their hold and carried them back, one at a time, and found that they fitted perfectly into their respective niches. One settled down with the break in his shell fitting like a machined tool into the break on the edge of the form. When he drew down, no power of mine could dislodge him. Then I put a strange limpet in the second place. He tried to settle, but his limy circumference did not fit; it was too narrow and had no break in the northwest rim. So he began to crawl away. Next I substituted the rightful owner

126

12. *Acapulco and Bay from a Hill-top.* Palms and bright flowers are scattered among the cactus in the landscape.

and all was well. This second animal I had found fifteen feet away on the down slope of a rock wholly out of even my sight of his home. I could trace his safari, however, by the narrow swath through the seaweed.

At the change of the tide, which was clock, time and season for these beings, they all turned, still feeding, and before the rock dried, they were back on their old stand, tight clamped, brooding on whatever limpets know to brood upon.

Once settled down, a limpet is impervious to any ordinary attack by any reasonable enemy. More than a century ago Walter Scott wrote, "He stuck like a lampit to a rock," and this is the limpet's quality of qualities. Given warning, and even the tip of a knife cannot be inserted beneath his person. Whether by the judicious seepage of some weak acid, or by sheer attrition, these big fellows are just sufficiently counter-sunk into the rock to make their socket impregnable.

Other kinds of limpets have an oblong hole at the summit of their shelly wigwams; they are known as key-hole limpets. But the great limpets of Tangola-Tangola—*Patella mexicana*, conchologists call them—lived in solid, massive, concrete tents; the lock was spiked, the key thrown away and the combination wholly lost in a passive resistance which should confine their Enemy Number One to Old Age.

Somehow as I sat and watched my limpet city, my mind went back to a time three decades ago, on the opposite side of the world, when I sat in a Chinese houseboat and looked at one of the strangest of cities. It too had quaint roofs, it was built on mighty rocks and it also had a feeling of quiet capability. It was on the Yangtze River, at the entrance of the great gorges, and its name was Ichang. So before I left

127

13. Acapulco, Mexico. A corner of the market reveals the origin of the five-cent store.

my Tangola-Tangola city of limpets, I printed the word "ICHANG" very blackly, and erected it in a cleft stick. I felt it was appropriate because in Chinese it means "Fitting Prosperity," and I thought the limpets would like that if only they could know. But they are serious all their lives. They can neither read nor give way to occasional, silly, unscientific fancies such as mine.

CHAPTER XII

SALVADOR—DE OMNIBUS REBUS

WHEN we alleged civilized folk desert our cities and go to far, clean, open lands there is much that we have to shed or molt or discard. We might even begin with the silly, unnecessary odds and ends of clothing, for when we get down to sneakers, shorts, a shirt and occasionally a hat we have acquired a comfort and freedom which no collar, tie or trousers ever confer. As our nostrils are gradually purged of nicotine, leather, gasoline, smoke and other man-made odors, a whole new world of delectable smells becomes manifest, and we can sniff and ecstatically wrinkle our noses in a new and precious code of etiquette of the sea and the jungle. All this is even more true of mental quirks. Reared as we are on atlases and maps it is always a shock to pass from one country to another and find that after all one is not purple and the other orange.

For weeks we had been coasting along the western shore of Mexico, poking our bow into every likely looking bay. Now, when we left Tangola, we sailed southward as fast as possible across the Gulf of Tehuantepec. The following day we watched an endless line of lovely, lofty sierras, almost too high and too symmetrical for reality. The glass showed a cluster of houses which was Champerico, and suddenly we realized that Guatemala was slipping past and would be for us only a line of great mountains and a cluster of red roofs.

Then, for a subconscious moment, came the small-boy wonder and a renewed examination through binoculars for something un-Mexican and pro-Guatemalan. All the geography
colours of our youth were washed out. Even the ocean life—
skipjacks, mackerel, flyingfish, shearwaters and dolphins—all
were the same as off Mexico. One thing, however, Guatemala
offered which I shall not forget—the superb volcano of Santa
Maria, with a side shoulder pouring forth white smoke. Slowly,
quietly, eternally, the cloud which was not a cloud, wound
upward. Like the old smoke language of the Navajo Indians,
this new land had signaled me, "Look! I am different!" and
I grinned and said, "Thanks," and liked Guatemala.

On the morning of the thirteenth of December, both
Stormy Pete, our grand captain, and his chart insisted that
the same old coastline was now still another country, Salvador.
To me this stood only for a page of stamps in an album. I do
not want to convey the idea that we leaped from Mexico to
Salvador because of fear of fierce Tehuantepecker storms. Our
route was controlled for the most part by bays, and Guatemala's coast seemed too smooth and even, on the chart, to
suggest good shelter and collecting.

We had to stop at El Salvador's port of La Libertad to wait
for the arrival of the Santa Rosa with mail, frozen meat and
other supplies, otherwise we should have missed seeing some
lovely, some shocking and some unexpected things. Anchor-
ing off the port, we found it, geographically, the kind of place
we should never have visited had it not been for the demands
of our iceboxes. But before we left Salvador we blessed that
lack.

I found a small volume in the captain's cabin called The

Commercial Travelers' Guide to Latin America, and from it I acquired a most amazing amount of useless, jumbled information. "Salvador," I read, "is the most densely populated of Latin countries, with 109 inhabitants per square mile." Hearing a flood of Spanish, I looked up and saw a launchful of pompous little Salvadorian officials alongside. In fact, there were exactly eleven of them, so that somewhere, one-tenth of a square mile on shore had been depopulated (according to my Latin guidebook).

The poor dears were overdressed, buttoned much too tightly, so full of dignity that even the low bulwark was an effort, ultra polite, with many asides, some of which I could understand. I once had a little monkey who tortured himself for no reason at all by often looking up into the trees, or into the far distance, when he was dying to touch or examine or eat something within reach, but completely selfconscious because of my presence. The sad rusty pier and the sadder shore held much of the attention of our visitors when they were bursting to concentrate on the yacht and our scientific gadgets. It was the last word in inferiority complex. But two or three short, quick, strong ones refocused their whole beings. They unbuttoned themselves, physically and mentally, they poured over everything, they filled the air with hissing Spanish epithets of admiration. Thus by the judicious application of a moderate quantity of C_2H_5OH, the status of uncomfortable alien visitors had changed to that of friendly buddies. How great is chemistry!

When at last they saw our collections of fish in the laboratory they broke loose in the universal language of anglers. Faster and faster came the spate of Spanish until all separation into words ceased. The last shred of translation passed from me and yet the gist of it all was "Wedontcallthatalargeoneinsalvador!" Finally they signed our papers with happy flourishes, and most reluctantly they allowed the tenth of some square mile on shore to swallow them again. They were all grand hombres.

To say that La Libertad was an open roadstead is an understatement. From a horizon-long stretch of sand and straggly growth a spindly-legged steel pier reached far out toward us through an incredible number of breakers. The chief exports (so said my book) are "coffee, sugar, balsam, indigo, hats, honey and hides." Being Commercial Travelers neither in honey, hides nor hats, no machinery was set in motion for us, and we scrambled and clutched our way, as best we could, into Salvador. For the purchasers of indigo and balsam a little double seat is usually swung out to the boat by a crane. We had to brace ourselves and balance carefully as successive swells raised us six feet to heaven and then dropped us a fathom down toward the bottom of the sea. At the moment of greatest ascension we seized any reachable rung of a slippery iron ladder, and forthwith scuttled up out of the way. Our carcinologist almost came to grief because an extremely rare crab chose this moment out of all time to walk across an adjacent pile, and it took all our cries in English, and an equal but shriller volume in Spanish, to persuade her to let the crab go and preserve her life.

We walked down the pier with dozens of great swells rolling past, finally to break on the black lava sand. We watched with fascinated interest the Thursday ablutions of the Libertadian women and children, the former being clad in awful, full-length calico gowns. The process consisted in rushing full speed down to the edge of the last receding wave, scooping up a gourdful of water cum sand, pouring it inside the front of the bedraggled wrappers or over the heads of the infants, and then fleeing for safety far up the beach. This was repeated until apparently complete exhaustion put an end. In this way modesty was achieved a full one hundred per cent, but cleanliness I should be inclined to rate at about a tenth.

We walked through the hot, silent streets of the noontime siesta. From what we could see, the natives must be pitifully poor, and we marveled at the multiplicity of tiny shops and boxlike stores. Everyone must live by selling minute quantities of things to everyone else. Yet there were grilles set in adobe windows, even when the front door was broken beyond repair; an infinitesimal promenade and plaza had a floorless band stand, with jungle plants pushing up and elbowing aside the bulbless electric fixtures. The grackles and ground doves alone seemed to benefit by the general deterioration. Earthquakes had frolicked with the pavement and the attention of the usual evening parade of men and girls must often have been diverted from flirtation to watching their step.

To us, dining on the deck of the Zaca, the evening was sheer glory, a succession of pageants; first, a magnificent sunset with the afterglow from that red-hot sun setting fire to the cold clouds hanging over La Libertad. Later, far away, from some active volcano, there arose the dull glow of unquenched fires of earth; and lastly there floated overhead the almost full moon, glowing but quite dead.

Early on the seventeenth day of December we donned

unaccustomed clothing and again climbed the pier. A station wagon, so ancient that it gave us a feeling of complete security, awaited us and we started for San Salvador, the capital of El or just Salvador. Our backbones soon vibrated in rhythm with Mr. Ford's conveyance, and the scenery became ever more and more splendid. We climbed and climbed, skirting the knife-edge summits of spurs, arroyos and barrancas. Soon we had a distant and last view of the sea, doing a sort of reverse Balboa, and the majestic sierras fairly walked toward us.

The blobs of mud huts scattered here and there, were each encased in a glory of bougainvillia and poinsettia run riot. For many miles every speck of level or reasonably oblique ground was covered with coffee or maize. The huts were so few that I expected, sooner or later, to see a place where the native mestizos were standing shoulder to shoulder, to balance my book's estimate of "109 per square mile." Our driver was enthusiastic about side trips for which we had no time. When he suggested turning aside to visit a place called *Zacatecoluca*, we thought he was being funny in English slang, or that it was some place which would afford another view of the sea far behind us, and the yacht, until we suddenly realized he was still talking Spanish and referred to a populous town which (my book again) "was hardly worth a visit by Commercial Travelers."

Houses improved and soon we passed estates lovely with flowers, country clubs and golf links. The overhanging volcano of Salvador rose higher as we approached its base, calm now, although it had broken forth and destroyed the city less than twenty-five years before. An attractive lake has gradually formed near its slopes, and the driver told us that very soon this must be dynamited and drained, since its increasing weight would result in terrible earthquakes. This was verified later by a geologist whom we met. On the farther side of the city was a smaller peak, raising its head dusty and quiescent, which only a year before meted out death to ten thousand people near its base. Several times a day I am sure we all looked up rather apprehensively at these splendid peaks, but no native seemed ever to give them a thought.

At last we entered the narrow streets of San Salvador and engaged enormous, cool rooms at the Hotel Nuevo Mundo. Our driver still hung around, chagrined at our disappointment at seeing so little bird life on the way. Suddenly his eye brightened, and he begged us to come and see *"todos los pájaros de Salvador, muy cerca."* So we went a few blocks to find our objective, a little bird store with a few miserable tanagers and mockers. There were, however, two lovely solitaires, one beginning to whisper his incomparable notes beneath his breath.

Our next drive was to the Museo Nacional. This was housed in two large rooms connected by an outdoor covered passageway. To reach it we had to dispute the right of way with most friendly and affectionate burros and cows. The outdoor space was apparently the Zoo Nacional, as it was filled with a few old wire cages with white rats, guinea-pigs and rabbits, together with a pair of despondent spider monkeys, a caracara and a raven. One of the monkeys was working with thumbless futility at a loose nail in its wire.

The natural history room was partly blocked at the entrance by a case containing a double-headed calf, mounted or rather stuffed in a confusion of bodies and legs which defied understanding. At the sides of the room and down the center were small cases, literally falling apart and indescribably dusty. The entomological collection consisted of about one hundred butterflies which had been mounted in plant presses, for their bodies were as flat as their wings. The only lepidoptera which were thriving were the clothes moths which were having a grand time with the remains. The central case contained a pelican with pouch so distended with straw that it almost obscured the rest of the bird. A moth-eaten canary was half falling out of a nest made of cast-off cotton threads, while her eyeless spouse clung hopelessly to a wire branch above, defying all the laws of gravitation and of ornithological anatomy.

In the wall cases were several hundred abominably made bird skins, hung up by their feet. Some, beneath the dust, were just recognizable as caciques and others as tanagers and herons; many were literally skins, with all the feathers in piles on the floor of the case. They were labeled, and in the absence of any guard and without much trouble I forced open a door and reached in. The labels bore nothing but the native name and a date; no collector or place. A few mastodon bones, molars and vertebrae were almost coated with feathers which had dropped from the birds overhead.

A few Mayan idols, a lot of beautiful black, obsidian arrow points, and some breastplates, spurs and chests of the old conquistadores completed the Museum. Last but not least was a railed off, stained park bench on which an early president, his wife and daughter had been assassinated during a revolution.

We found out that the collection as a whole was the work

of another president who had also been shot or stabbed about fifteen years before. Salvador has evidently been no place for a scientist. Like a few of our northern museums this of San Salvador was in the Stone Age of Science; it was almost worse than nothing. Let me add that no exaggeration has crept into this description. I have presented in accurate detail the Museo Nacional, and I have done this with the hope that soon Salvador will awaken to the wonders of her birds and beasts and butterflies of her forests and mountains. I would like to see added to her "coffee, sugar, balsam, indigo, honey and hides" the interest to her own people and to visitors of a splendid zoo and museum. ¡Viva ciencia in Salvador!

After a long walk through much of the city, three things were impressed upon us—we were the only tourists, thank heaven, there was a circus opening this very evening, and although the great day was a week away, the spirit of Christmas was rampant. In place of political and advertising posters were huge placards, ¡Viva Christos Rey! There were no beggars, and good manners characterized every class. Two little boys asked timidly if they could direct us anywhere, and in answer to my question one said that we must go to the telegraph office, have nothing to do with the operator, but ask for Jesus, who was the best guide there was. We agreed, and tipped him, but in the light of the full moon went our unregenerate way alone. Polite, considerate reporters interviewed us, and the following morning we found that even the stigma of turistas had been removed, and we had become científicos.

A few blocks from our hotel we sighted the exciting circus lights and tent-top, but we almost regretted going in because every step thither was entertainment beyond price to our

northern, Anglo-Saxon eyes. For the sum of seventy-five centavos we were admitted to the palco, which is Salvadorian for
ringside seats, and our knees and toes were practically inside
the twelve-inch red cloth which delimited the tanbark. A
trapeze and tight-rope nearly over our heads and a tiny ring
made us settle down with contented sighs. There were no
peanuts or pink lemonade, but delicious *cerveza* and *dulces*.

The audience in the bleachers numbered a hundred or
more, mostly barefooted, bright-rebosoed peons and Indians,
and quite a number of people in our reserved palco. There
were two small, draped board boxes, all on the bare earth,
one of which was marked "Colonel Fachendoso." Soon the
Colonel and some family filed in, and looked at us aloofly as
through lorgnettes. We didn't care for them and watched
them hopefully, for we had seen a large tarantula creep over
and into their box, and we longed for an unrehearsed act.
But the spider had probably crawled into its hole in this erstwhile vacant lot, and the snooty ones had no scare.

Suddenly a whistle blew and a splendid eight-man marimba
band struck up within twenty feet of where we sat and played
throughout the whole two hours plus of the performance,
never too loud and often so softly that they formed a delightful obligato to what was going on. Rumba, Sousa, over-
tures, Viennese waltzes, they played all uncommonly well.
Behind us, several rows back, sat a man and a woman who
were hardly real. She had huge features, made up beyond
belief, and hair dyed blonde with long dangling curls, and
she was wholly unselfconscious, an exaggeration of Charley's
Aunt. With her was a giant of a man with broken nose, scars
everywhere and a general caste of face as unbelievable as hers,

We had a difficult time to keep from staring. They were like masks, caricatures of the Worst-woman-in-the-world and the typical Worst-bandit. Well built but twice the size of the peons around them, they were perfectly well-behaved, laughing and applauding like children. Again it seemed as if it all was for our benefit, a Hollywood set inexcusably overdone, with us alive in the foreground.

Across the ring was an Indian family, the man with fine high nose, and magnificent Mayan profile, the woman with hair to her waist, nursing a baby and wholly absorbed in everything that happened. The man who played the drums and other gadgets with such intricate and interchanging rhythm, as only a Latin American could, was another face never-to-be-forgotten. As he drummed or even when tapping and muting a cymbal, he looked off into space, completely engrossed, hypnotized. He had wide-flaring nostrils, high cheek bones and infinitely sad eyes, combined with a strange, constantly searching, unfocused look, glancing everywhere in the intervals of playing, as if looking for something but dreading to find it. This sounds silly, melodramatic and absurd, but we all separately sensed it. It was a face with fine and equally evil possibilities.

I was so interested in the marimba playing that I slowly drifted over, close to the players, and watched them before the show started. When they finished the first piece I instinctively applauded heartily as did we all, but no one else. We had very evidently made a Salvadorian social faux pas, but nevertheless the face of the drummer lit up amazingly with a smile and then the mask settled down again. Near the entrance side of the palco the party of *correctos* or well-to-do people looked condescendingly about them at first, but afterwards broke down and enjoyed everything as much as anyone. Rather softly but consistently, after every special event, we clapped gently, and before the show was over we had quite a claque who joined amateurishly in with us. Perhaps we established a new custom of audible appreciation in San Salvador.

A little boy in long trousers came out with a rush, looked around with what he pretended was astonishment, and bowed with what someone has called "pleased surprise" at sight of the audience. He was lifted up to a trapeze and while a man stood beneath to catch him if he fell, he did some excellent balancing with and without a chair. Then a clown sang a very funny song with dozens of refrains, the humor of which evaded us entirely. In fact, all the high, or rather, obviously low comedy of the evening was tantalizingly nebulous to us, while the audience rocked. A slack-rope walker was surprisingly good, turning back somersaults. He and his long metal balancing pole were directly over my head, so I at first prayed for his skill, and later blessed it, as otherwise one *científico* would have been carried down to the coast on a shutter.

Came more clown and then a very lovely senorita in tights and spangles who sang a topical song to the delight of everyone including ourselves. After this a man changed water to rice before our eyes and made a pack of cards vanish with somewhat insufficient speed. Then several clowns with helpers, and a man and a boy with a wooden barrel. Father balanced and juggled the barrel on his feet as he lay on his back, and then cleverly juggled the boy. Finally two acrobats did as high trapeze as the tent permitted, after ten minutes of

140

net stretching below. Once, when one man slipped, we could hear the gasp of breath as his partner let him fall. They too were really good, and the singing senorita was terribly worried about the one who fell.

Next came a rather sad little circus pinto pony and a black dog. The dog rode the horse as the horse jumped low sticks and then, by dint of scraping him off the saddle blanket, the dog was made to seem to jump. When he failed, as he mostly did, the horrible woman who had the whip gave the assisting clown such a look as would have driven me to the mountains in terror of my life. We unanimously hated that woman.

Then the ever-pleasant senorita came out and danced a rumba and all was well again. Finally the clowns, and all the company unsuccessfully disguised, joined in an intricate farce, linguistically far over our heads, but emotionally only too apparent, after which the giant Negro who moved the scenery rushed on with a flaming torch, chased all the actors and performers away and everyone except ourselves knew that the circus was over. The moonlight and the pleasant Indian and edible smells outside, and the glimpses through the doors into the patios made it all seem like life on another planet compared with ours on the Zaca.

My room, which was enormous and with a ceiling so high that it seemed as if stars ought to be shining above me, looked out on a plaza with a filling station and a stand for a dozen cars along the edge. I went to bed a little after midnight and listened for a while. At one o'clock a roaring arose like the beginning of a volcanic outbreak, soon changing into a whistling howl behind the hotel. Then came the squeal of brakes, toots for the filling-station man, half-tone double horns, cracked shrieks from broken calliopes—all this almost continuous. Then the church bells began for some untemporal reason, with seven or eight *gang! gang! gangs!* then a rest, then seven or sometimes nine. It was like the Indian brain-fever bird, these bellbirds of Salvador. Having made up my mind to listen and enjoy it, I promptly went to sleep and did not waken until six o'clock. The sun leaped up and all the midnight pandemonium redoubled, with the addition of untold numbers of firecrackers in honor of the coming Christmas. The Salvadorians cannot have snow, but they can have gunpowder and they do. I counted eighteen kinds of automobile horns, between six and seven o'clock.

Then came burro-drawn carts with old frying pans hung beneath and stone clappers pounding against them, as guards against scorching automobiles. Wooden hammers of ice-cream vendors, and street cries running the gamut of the human vocal chords from rumbling bass to highest C's. I shrieked in sympathy in the shower and could hardly hear myself, and then went down to a delicious breakfast.

We reveled in the markets all the morning. As I have said, we were the only tourists in the city, and nine-tenths of the customers were Indians or peons with cinco centavos as the outside limit for any one purchase. So all the stocks in trade were geared to this economy. The result was to put to utter shame any five-and-ten-cent store ever conceived in northern marts. Christmas, only a week away, was the motive everywhere. Along the gutters of the streets bordering the markets were hundreds of small stalls, mostly without coverings, and with old newspapers or great leaves spread on the ground as

142

14. *Young Pacific Sailfish.* This infant is only one and five-eighths of an inch in length, the smallest ever taken. It was captured at the night light, twenty-three miles off-shore from Uvita, Costa Rica.

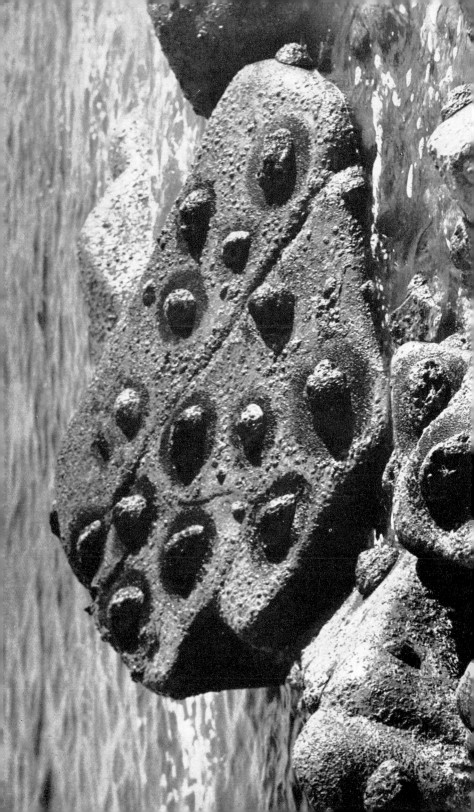

counters and show cases. Here were thousands upon thousands of tiny clay images, all made by hand, from minute beings less than an inch long, to three-foot dragon-like creatures born of untrammeled imaginations. There were women patting tortillas with dishes of most realistic edibles around, a woman with a machete killing a turkey, and hosts of single creatures, armadillos, guinea hens, vultures, squirrels, soldiers, clowns, saints and washerwomen. All were made by Indians in the vicinity of San Vicente. Some were crude and hardly recognizable, a great many showed extreme beauty and anatomical knowledge, some slavishly representing every muscle, others fashioned in the most modernistic style. Since all were handwork, no two were exactly alike. Most of the little figures were brightly painted and had practical stands, and the average price was five centavos, or two cents American. We began to buy and then realized we had no way of carrying them, so went into the market proper and purchased baskets of varied shapes and gorgeous patterns.

The dominant theme, as I have said, was Christmas and the materials of the cheapest. There were thousands of Christ childs, all pink, lying with a tiny bit of white cloth about their middles. Equal numbers of burros lay or even sat, together with cows and sheep, but no goats. Local color was occasionally introduced into the diminutive Noel crèches, and often in place of the attendant burros and cows, there were realistic spoonbills, zopilotes and armadillos. It was easy to visualize and excuse the workings of the Indian mind which fashioned these sweet little tableaux, in unconsciously populating the villages of Palestine with unmistakable neotropical

143

15. *Giant Limpets of Tangola-Tangola.* Each is resting in its home niche, waiting for the rising tide.

fauna. The owner of one stall was attempting to establish a new motif in manger decorations, and in these the Christ child looked up at a background of coloured pages from Sears, Roebuck or Stumpp & Walter catalogues, while bat-like birds of flaming red hovered on wires over the heads of the Holy Family. In the mind of this artist there appeared to exist a certain confusion between Santa Claus and the virgin birth, because in a dozen tableaux an obvious Santa in white beard and red jacket looked benignly down on the manger. Here, too, was the only attempt at cottony snow, which must have been incomprehensible to most of the Indian onlookers, and the presence of which in the Bethlehem stable carried a suspicion of hyperbole.

The allegories were fascinating; the devil in black and gold pushing a woman, apparently not too unwilling; another fiend holding a ball of gold with silver circles on it representing filthy lucre; still another with spread bat-wings clutching a diminutive bottle, with at least two dozen more bottles strewing the ground.

We bought recklessly, and returned again and again, so that the people got to recognize us and rushed off to get new things to tempt the millionaire scientists who apparently possessed endless numbers of cinco centavos. One booth had piles of sections of huge posters, incomplete sheets of well-known cigarette brands, or the lower, right-side quarter of Greta Garbo's face. These were selling briskly, probably intended for wall paper in distant huts.

The market proper seemed to go on and on for miles, with hundreds of stalls with baskets, rebosas, flowers, real and artificial, woven cloths of great beauty from Guatemala, saddles giving forth delicious leather smells, shoes, and a central court with immense piles of earthenware vases, ollas, jars and dishes. Unless we were very vigilant we would almost step on the tiniest of tiny babies crawling nakedly about on their occasions, and when we left a basket for a few minutes we would look carefully inside to make sure that no infant was curled up asleep. Vegetable, meat, fish, grain, all had piles of very small cornucopias with single vegetables, and almost countable grains for the inevitable cinco centavos.

We watched an Indian family buying a small Christ, and for minute after minute the talk would go on, the choice wavering between a very small one with a burro couchant, or a larger, pinker one alone. Toward the end I had an admiring crowd following me, watching the treasures go into my great baskets. I staged an exciting scene over a little tableaux of seven zopilotes or vultures, red heads and all, on a paper and wire tree, all wriggling delightfully on their individual wires, while on the ground below was a blotch and mound of something awful in bright yellow with purple spots. I demanded to know on what the vultures were feeding before I would purchase. "*¿Que comen los zopilotes?*" I asked, and the whole street giggled. People collected. A truckman blew his horn, but no one paid any attention so he climbed down, elbowed in and giggled with the rest. At last the girl owner answered, "*Muertos.*" This would not do as I demanded what *muertos?* Someone prompted "*Carne.*" I tentatively suggested "*¿Hombre?*" but this brought down a whole chorus of "*¡No, no, Señor; nunca hombre!*" with a note of seriousness threatened, so I acquiesced and at last an urchin screamed "¡Perro!" After a long discussion in which at least ten persons joined, we all agreed that *perro* was right and I made the purchase, I think to everyone's regret because it put an end to this excitement.

CHAPTER XIII

A VOLCANO'S CHILD

BECAUSE of our specialized desires and needs in scientific collecting, the Zaca and we had to be very choosey about our bays. If they were too small we could hardly enter and maneuver; if too big, they were unprotected and all but impossible. The Gulf of Fonseca came under the latter head.

From La Libertad we went south all night, and while at breakfast on deck next morning we passed between two great islands not unlike 'Statius and St. Kitts in the Antilles. In the distance, Volcan San Miguel signaled from the depths of Mother Earth with an unending series of shrapnel bursts of white cloud steam. As we went on, the water got muddier, the current swifter, boobies fell behind and mangrove swallows appeared; we were in the Gulf of Fonseca.

After a tussle with the tide we made fast to the long pier at La Union, at the southernmost tip of Salvador. Our view at first was of a forest of piles, through which the water swirled, and whose tenants were crabs, barnacles, fish and snails. Slowly, on a third dimension of the same tide, we rose, foot after foot, yard upon yard, until our deck topped the pier and we again saw sky and swallows, and a German freighter with a friendly but bored baby elephant making an undesired trip from Hamburg to Honolulu. We walked up the pier and a mile or more to the town of La Union. I recall

147

carts with great wheels of solid wood, four-eyed fish, millions of arca shells, tepid fizzy water and sizzling hot air. All the charm of San Salvador was absent. (Plate 17.)

We spent six days in this great gulf, chiefly because of eternal delays in getting oil, supplies and mail. It was more than a case of mañana—it approximated nunca. We should have welcomed such enforced stay almost anywhere else, but while the Tehuantepeckers had been left behind, the Papagayos had found us out. For some unknown reason this word, which means "parrot" in both Spanish and German, here signified an eternal continental draft, a pain in the neck of our researches, blowing through the open window in the wall of the mighty Sierra Mountains. It is a whole-winter affair, from November to April, so if you are a native you either get used to it or go crazy. The mornings would break as perfectly as possible for any day, quiet, calm, clear. Then about nine o'clock a zephyr would cool our cheeks, and in another hour a steady blow would stir up the muddy water, and the distant shore would be shut off from us by series of smashing breakers. The gulf bounded by Salvador, Honduras and Nicaragua became, for much of the day, a churned-up cauldron, putting an end to all fishing and seining, and even landing except on the lee-est of lee shores. We shuttled back and forth to such places as Fumerole, Meanguera, Farallones, Rio Potosi and Monypenny Point, and everywhere we went the Papagayo followed. Fate must have something in store for our future, for not a boat was overturned, not one of us drowned, but not for lack of opportunity. In desperation I went down in the helmet off the Zaca, but I never reached bottom. The current took me, together with hose, helmet and ladder, and

148

stretched us out taut and almost horizontal, and with all my breath gone I barely managed to fight my way up a few rungs, within reach of dehelmeting hands.

The fumerole, infant of the volcano, had the fascination of all volcanic activity. One of the most tragic and yet probably safest things about the human mind is the ease with which the greatest, most stupendous, significant cosmic phenomena become invisible, nonexistent to our conscious, appreciative minds. This is why, like brushing one's teeth, I put as necessities in our lives the frequent looking at the moon through an opera glass, and the thought of sunsets as earth-rises, of air as a tangible thing and not empty space. When, on the way into this great gulf, I saw smoke rising from the shore, a glance through the glass showed no fishermen cooking their breakfast, but a chimney-top of Mother Earth herself.

We landed in a cove several hundred yards away, and even here had to fight against the waves and hold our perishable collecting kit high over our heads. The beach was composed of huge, rounded boulders, over which we had to crawl on all fours. From the Zaca we appeared as an unlovely pack of awkward, inept apes creeping slowly and painfully along. Bubbling sounds were soon heard, and we came to the fumerole itself, boiling water being blown forth and spattered high in air, while steam poured up between the drops. Only the faintest hint of sulphur was detectable. A considerable area was too heated to stand on, and the escaping water remained hot until it reached the surges and cooled in the ocean. Here and there were unfortunate crabs, boiled to a scarlet hue, and well-done snails.

My curiosity led me to dig down, with the aid of two sticks, into the heated area. With a strong lever I tumbled over a good-sized boulder, received a spattering of boiling drops in my face, and diverted a small trickle of bubbling water. After I had cooled off, I followed this new streamlet and found that I had unwittingly wrought havoc with the fauna of five, little, under-stone worlds; crabs, snails, worms, starfish—all were being boiled before they could escape. With deep chagrin at having produced this multiple Pompeii, I confined my researches in volcanology to less destructive channels. (Plate 18.)

Old as Earth Herself as were such manifestations, living creatures seemed to have no means of being warned, and flies and bees constantly flew into the deadly area and crumpled. We watched the boiling water, we looked at the distant living volcano, we recalled the terrific local earthquakes, and the land hereabouts seemed very young and unreliable indeed; continuity with the first appearance of the continents, the preceding whirling ball of gas, the galaxies, seemed complete. The Zaca and ourselves became evanescent objects of the most recent seconds of the cosmic time-clock. I, at least, picked up my bag and started off with some vague idea of accomplishing something before a few additional seconds could snuff out body and imagination. I promptly slipped and fell between two boulders, barked my shins, and in the temporary pain my newly aroused cosmic consciousness ceased to exist.

Meanguera Island tempted us to go ashore by its smallness and sheer beauty. The green of the lofty trees was everywhere picked out with solid masses of delicate lilac—forty-foot bignonias, *Taberbuia pentaphyla*, or, as we preferred, *Flor de*

Cortez. The island was steep, a single mountain, and everywhere on the slopes were slanting toy cultivated fields, and obliquely founded huts and houses. The people were dark, gay, friendly, gave us fruits, caught us beetles, and finally lured us to the top of their mountain. They would not tell us what lay there, but urged us on. The way was steep and rocky—Bunyan had a name for it—and the foliage and purple vistas increased in loveliness, until we came out on the great, flat, bare summit. Here was rich soil, easy of cultivation, yet not a plant was there. Instead, there were lines of rough benches, and two immense wooden goals at either end. In short, before us, unbelievably, was a full-sized soccer field.

The Meanguerians watched us eagerly for approval. Would we play? They were, as we saw, *muy deportivos*. No, we were too hot to play, and our time was up, but we praised their soccer field, and never ceased to wonder at this un-Latin sacrifice of agriculture to *La Sport*. Such delightful, unexpected, unreasonableness brought to mind Drinkwater's "Feckenham Men":

> "Wheat-ricks," they said, "be good to see;
> What would a rick of blossoms be?"

After dark that evening, our friends came off in a small fleet of dugouts—the men only; we could see the women watching wistfully from the dim shore. They were allowed to board us and line the bulwarks. They listened with open mouths to our phonograph and radio; they watched with grinning approval as we drank our cocktails; not an eye ever left us as we ate, rather selfconsciously. Later, Pemasa Utu, our Samoan genius, danced for them in his scarlet-flowered lava-lava. At last they themselves were put through an examination of all the native names which they knew for fish and crabs.

Then they gently bade us *buenas noches* and went back to their mountain village, not to sleep, I am quite sure, but to discuss this evening of opera-cum-theater-cum-circus-cum-cinema all rolled into one for them.

Almost our last memory of this great, wind-torn gulf was of a perfect Christmas party, snug within a solid shelter of canvas dodgers around the deck, where a real Christmas tree, hundreds of coloured electric lights and gifts of many days' planning were unforgettable ingredients. Even the Papagayo helped, for its occasional gusts provided a sound effect of a wintry blizzard, until we peered out and saw the palms of Monypenny Point, and the Southern Cross all askew.

CHAPTER XIV

MANGROVE MAGIC

THOROUGHLY beaten by the eternal wind, we set our course out to sea, and looped south through all one night. At dawn *el volcan* Viejo rose before us from the Nicaraguan landscape still wearing its nightcap of cloud, while to the north Telica was already awake, pouring forth smoke which slipped slowly down its ravines and valleys. This was our introduction to the Bay of Corinto which was satisfactorily small and in the heart of a wilderness of mangroves. These stand everywhere on spindly stilts of roots in glistening mud, or wade knee-deep at high tide. (Plate 19.)

Corinto itself is one of the saddest towns I have ever known. Until a few years ago we had cruisers and several hundred marines stationed here, when governmental troubles of the country required it. Our leathernecks constituted a gold rush of sorts, and brought about a quick boom town growth, including two great hotels with ultra-elaborate bars, and an out-size plaza. Now the forlorn natives are few in number, the streets thick with grass in the daytime, and in the evening dismally and most inadequately lighted; long stretches of houses are unoccupied and the shops are wholly without interest.

A ghastly siren suddenly shrieked out, but instead of a fire or a revolution, it was merely notice that the cinema was about to begin. We attended but soon left. The chief interest lay in watching the lips of the actors as speeches and ejaculations poured forth, and then, after a comfortable stretch of time, a glaring Spanish title announced "¡El dice, 'Si!'" I half expected Roland Young to step out of the dreadful picture in disgust, to follow and join us at the nearest bar.

Much has been written of mangroves and their strange world—I have done it myself—and the bromidic catch phrase, "Land of a Single Tree," is as well known as the Himalayan tag of the "Roof of the World." But still the strangeness eludes description, and the heart of this association of plant and animal life is still dimmed with our ignorance.

We looked eastward from the deck of the *Zaca* as she swung at her Corinto anchorage, and the horizon was a level stretch of green. This was the outer, pioneer growth of the mangrove wilderness, and was worthily named *Isla Encantada* —the Enchanted Island. (Plate 20.)

On the occasion of my first visit to this island, as I stepped out into shallow water, my feet sank into a deep drift of variegated snow—or so it appeared. As far as I could see up and down the beach, the beauty held. I scooped up double handfuls of lovely shells, all alike, all different, tinkling together like an infinity of precious gems. They were olivellas. Why the name "olives" or "olivellas" I am at a loss to understand, unless we admit the misconstructive etymology of "little ovals." From one-half to three-quarters of an inch was the usual size, with graceful elongate mouth, and about three tightly rolled, tapering volutions. In fact, their specific name is an echo of their descriptive characters—*Olivella volutella*, a term which Lamarck conferred in one of his happier moments.

I shoveled up thousands of the delicate shells and ran them like larger grains of sand through my fingers, and when I stopped and looked carefully, I failed to find any two alike. Some were pale slate with the basal portion orange, or pink on the large whorl, while others were ivory-white with blood-red seams between, or clouded with wavy bands of gray, set off by rich brown. All were empty, all apparently washed up from some source of infinitely great olivella populations. (Plate 21.)

We went on up the main tidal waterway, and on for miles into smaller and smaller channels, twisting and turning until our boat actually grounded on marshy land, where we caught glimpses of apparently amphibious cattle. There was no need to blaze our way, although every mangrove looked exactly like all the other millions, and although en route we boxed nine-tenths of the compass. In order to retrace our steps we simply drifted with the ebbing tide, and always chose larger and larger openings. Patient herons were everywhere, motionless as those on Japanese screens, waiting for low tide; gaudy crabs scuttled around the arching roots, which in turn were braided with sleeping snails, and frilled with oysters.

As we paddled along the tortuous channels, unexpected things happened, as when something fell from an overhead branch into the water near by and drenched us with spray. The only person who was watching said it was a very short and thick snake, but I had seen an iguana in the air before, and knew that the closely folded legs in the dive would make a half glimpse fit this description. This stream-lined water dive

155

gains interest when we know that when the same lizard leaps from a lofty tree-top it spread-eagles to fullest extent to help break its fall on to scrub, and incidentally makes us believe that such performances were an important part in the beginning of flight in birds.

After this splash we watched more carefully, and saw big and little iguanas sunning themselves on the mangroves. These are among the few creatures which can afford to be individual as to colour and pattern. Our hunter brought in five one day, one of which was predominantly blackish, another green, a third banded with black and orange, while the largest, almost five feet in length, was quite tawny. One contained thirteen eggs about to be laid. Their food consisted entirely of young mangrove shoots and leaves. In their feeding they were as neat as a New England housewife. The leaves in a big lizard, perhaps two hundred in all, must have each been swallowed stem first, and right side up with the result that a generous portion of the digestive canal was filled with a solid line, which could be peeled apart into innumerable perfect leaves. These big iguanas should live safe, happy lives, diving, swimming and enjoying an unending succession of mangrove leaves.

This cosmos is peculiarly protected from invasion by many two- and four-legged creatures, such predators as men, monkeys, pumas and jaguars. Yet very few birds nest among the mangroves, the answer perhaps being the lack of dense, low foliage, the absence of necessary food, and the ease with which anacondas and other serpents can comb the branches.

At low tide a seining party went into the mangroves and tried to land on an exposed mudbank. The first two men

156

sank slowly, but with apparent prospect of complete ultimate submergence into the black, sticky mass. They were extracted with difficulty and to an accompaniment of epithets expressing distinct disapproval of the experience.

The only other method of unaided entrance by human beings was by climbing from arch to arch of what botanists call "pithy, lenticulate, arching prop roots." This looked easy, but when to the soap-like slipperiness of the roots are added their unpredictable yielding quality, the unattached bases of many and total lack of solid footing, progression was exhausting, painful and futile.

Night worked a magic in this region, which we discovered by accident. Late one afternoon we drifted slowly down the maze of outer channels. Mudbanks were being rapidly uncovered and birds became numerous. Spotted sandpipers trotted singly along the edge of the water and Hudsonian curlews were in twos and threes. Now and then they rose and went off through side passages with their wonderful notes ringing out. Alabaster egrets watched us pass, and not even an eyelid moved. A pair of fork-tailed flycatchers appeared in the treetops, and swooped swiftly, up, around and down, their tail feathers floating and curving after them. A snakebird climbed, awkward as a sea-lion on land, and two score white ibises were the loveliest of all the birds, long white streamers against the dark green set off with bright pink foreheads and beaks. Six parrakeets flew over screeching, and still higher, the vultures always watched us hopefully.

As we turned one of the last mangrove corners, we approached a rocky islet with a number of high trees. All but a single group were filled with all the frigatebirds in the world, and the dead and whitened branches showed that this had been their dormitory for a long time. Man-o'-war birds are most solitary throughout their daily activities, but here was a magnet which drew them from many miles every evening. The uppermost slender branches were the favorites. A loud hand clapping on our part roused the entire host, and all rose and circled about, like a cloud of enormous gnats geared down to slow motion. I watched eight birds trying to alight on a thin branch which would comfortably hold only about three. It took ten minutes of alighting, buffeting with their wings, slipping off and having to soar high up to make a new landing, before all were clinging precariously to the swaying perch.

On the same tiny island, a separate group of six smaller trees was the bedroom of the Corinto pelicans. None were actually touching, but they were so close together that a little perspective showed the trees as a solid mass of brown, humped-up figures, beakless, but with their eyes on the lookout for trouble from above the contour of the back. Five brown pelicans and two frigatebirds were sleeping on the nearest branches of mangroves, outlaws because of no more space, which in this case must be interpreted as squatting room only.

As we went on into the sunset, the afterglow grew into a marvelous intensity, staining the mangrove roots bright red, and the waters of the bay brilliant orange and salmon from the gold and scarlet clouds. To the north, at this moment, we caught sight of eight or nine hundred jet-black silhouettes passing slowly across the blazing background, and we knew that nearly a thousand unmistakable fork-tailed flycatchers were headed for their sleeping quarters somewhere in the heart of the hospitable mangroves.

158

16. *Bay of Guatulco.* The pelicans fly to roost in a perfect V-formation.

But even this did not end the night magic. A day or two later, from the *Zaca*, I saw a faint mist of dots moving high over the mangroves. They might have been a cloud of gnats fifty feet away, or sandpipers at a quarter mile, or innumerable vultures a full mile off. My "Sixes" were no use, and only "Number Twelves" resolved them definitely into birds. I watched until my eyes ached, for I had never seen so many feathered creatures at once. I was rewarded, for at last one dark mass veered and swung downward, and as they went, the rays of the setting sun painted them for a moment with pure emerald, and a thousand green meteors vanished below the mangrove horizon—Amazon parrots were my guess.

The next night I anticipated this marvelous sight, and went ashore on the distant Enchanted Island. I found a horizon opening and arranged myself comfortably on the beach. The multitudes appeared in the distance suddenly, without my seeing them arrive, four separate legions which shuttled back and forth, silhouetted against the sky. The flocks would almost fuse and then separate again, the fraying strands being always parrot-wise in twos, fours or sixes. For a long ten minutes they swung high in air, drawn like gray veils across the afterglow and the lavender cones of the distant volcanoes. A new flock came from nowhere, not more than a quarter mile away, and my focus was perfect, and I plainly saw the green colour, and suddenly the long, pointed tails. So they were not parrots but parrakeets or conures.

What amusing things our sense organs are! When I held the birds in focus, sitting breathless and openmouthed, I could distinctly hear the faint screaming from the thousands of throats. When I laboured with naked eyesight alone, the

159

17. *La Union, Salvador.* In the street, under the open sky, the people gossip, eat, drink, buy, sell and dry their coffee beans.

sound died to vanishing point, increasing a moment later, through the glasses. It seems impossible to record sense impressions of more than one kind simultaneously, with equal perception.

At every swoop of the hosts a few isolationists would ravel out, and a few pairs dive down, not to reappear. My fifth flock crossed and amalgamated with one of the others, and then the whole multitude hurled itself down in a final nose dive, and out of sight. No hint in the low, dead-level horizon line told of the sleeping tens of thousands of little, breathing forms. Scores of mangroves had their foliage doubled, as innumerable pairs of the parrakeets huddled close together on the branches, and apart from all other pairs. Without our man-made, high-power binoculars we should never have known what they were.

But the scientist in me was still far from satisfied. There are more than a dozen kinds of parrots and parrakeets in this general region, and how could I make certain of the exact species of this somnolent army? I offered a reward, then a larger one, a third more munificent. All no use; no one would venture into the fearsome mangroves at night; cosas, "things," floated there in the moonlight which it were ill to gaze upon.

As so often happens to me, proof came in a roundabout way. We were admiring the tarnished magnificence of Christie's bar in Corinto, when I was hailed by a stout, jolly person who recalled to me that in years past I used to buy birds from him, when I was building up the collection in the Zoological Society's Zoo. In the backyard of the bar were hundreds of small, sad-faced monkeys and parrots which he was taking to New York. He had none of my parrakeets, but knew of a boy who had caught one. The bird had fallen into the water after a fight with one of its kind, from a large, passing flock.

The boy was summoned and the bird changed hands for fifty centavos, or about twelve cents. It was perfectly tame and climbed about our persons, making contented little sounds, and gratefully accepting anything edible. Here were eleven inches of pleasant personality, clothed in greens of various attractive shades, from grass to apple. As we approached the *Zaca* I was externally merely the possessor of a new pet; within I felt the unpleasant symptoms of a Judas-like nature. On board, Perico immediately held court and happily received the approval of everyone. Only the cats watched the newcomer with unexpressive agate eyes, but a slight movement of the lips.

What I had to do, I had to do quickly, so while everyone was drinking cocktails I excused myself with some mumbled lie and went below. When I came up I had an extra quick one and probably exhibited futile enthusiasm about nothing in particular. One of my staff has a keen nose for chloroform and soon after dinner my crime was discovered and I became an outcast and a thing abhorred, and was reminded none too gently that even to the lowest savages the life of a guest is sacred. I protested something about the cats, and that Perico had passed away painlessly with a smile on her beak, but it did little good. At least she fulfilled a destiny of sorts and we now knew that the mangrove multitudes were *Aratinga holochlora strenua*, the Nicaraguan ivory-billed green parrakeet. At which my unsympathetic carcinologist remarked, "So what?"

CHAPTER XV

TIDEPOOLS: DAY AND NIGHT

WE had planned to stay two days in the Bay of Corinto, but eleven slipped past before our opportunities and discoveries ceased. The mangroves and the lagoon were partly to blame, but the principal magnet was the tidepools of Isla Cardon. This small island had a diminutive lighthouse on the bay side. We climbed to the steep bank by wooden steps suspended in mid-air, every other step of which teetered, or was broken or completely missing. Also the handrail often came away in our hands, but it was a crooked way which led to a paradise of living creatures.

A handful of so-called guards was on duty (using those words in the Cardonian sense). They were brought to life at the time of our first visit by an officer, not because they feared an invasion of enemy gringos, but because a senorita had been reported as climbing the landing stairs. It seemed to me that a new bugle call was invented on the spot which resulted in instantaneous, galvanized, superhuman efforts to collect and don sufficient clothing to permit them to meet the senorita without embarrassment. On the occasion of our second visit, their dominant emotion was curiosity, and was marked by a gift of fish and crabs, all very second-hand, and with difficulty staving off dissolution. They were a friendly, jolly crowd, and our visits must have divided all the time of their existence into two parts. The third and succeeding trips did not break the slumber of the Corintian guards, and Isla Cardon and its tidepools were all ours.

A hundred yards took us across the island and we looked down over a great foreshore of rolling, contorted lava. Three miles off the land was a British freighter drifting, standing by for our launch which, radio-summoned, was carrying our doctor. On the freighter a very sick man waited for a blood transfusion which was to save his life.

I walked down over the long slope to the edge of low tide, where slow, emerald, heaving swells reluctantly curved and broke into a million alabaster drops. Far down I could see long, waving seaweed, and big fish swaying back and forth with the currents. From here up to the fringe of land vegetation, lay outstretched the lava, its surface fretted with crevices and pot-holes of the grandest tidepools we had yet seen. They had been waiting thousands of years for our arrival, and their Aladdin treasures begged for study. My mind sought for a simile and my memory went back to barren hillsides swept clean by storms and sun-dried heat in the central Himalayas, with here and there an enclosed and sheltered hanging valley, well watered and solid with lush growth. Here the moon-pulled mass of the sea crept slowly up over all the shore, scouring the lava and periodically refreshing the deep pools with oxygen and food.

Today's invasion was hours off, and now each little pool waited patiently. The water in the pools was so clear that only a wetted finger-tip revealed its level, this and the sharp line between naked rock and the beginning of living tapestry. As I looked down I seemed to see a shore within a shore, for along the rim was a windrow of fine grains and broken bits of shell, like that bordering the sand beach farther down the island. But magic began at the very pool rim, for when I tried to brush this aside, it all began to move and shift. I found it was blanketing a thousand little dark-green anemones, and I never solved the mystery of how the upper ones acquired this protection against heat and dry air. The only way the mosaic of the patchwork quilt could reach them was by their brother anemones handing the bits up, firebucketwise from the bottom of the pool. Yet never have I seen any one anemone consciously do another a good turn. Perhaps each little being higher up on the rock reached down with its tentacles, stole a frayed-out remnant, and tucked itself in, only to have it in turn pulled off its anemone bed by a friend higher up who needed it badly. At any rate, the exposed organisms held aloft this dense canopy during the season of drought, exactly like the lattices and hangings which shade the narrow streets of an oriental city like Bagdad.

When I began scattering the bits of sand and shell, the unusual rain down through the water attracted a crowd of blennies and gobies, little kibitzers who came to see if anything besides bricks and mortar was falling, hoping for a few crumbs of manna. One horse-faced little chap stuck his head far between the arms of my forceps in his eagerness to snatch at a drifting morsel. As I have said before, someone should devote a whole book to these two groups of fish. They should be set apart from all other fish, if not by physical characters, then by sheer personality and psychology. In the main they are more akin to intelligent lizards than to any of their fellow poolers.

164

TIDEPOOLS: DAY AND NIGHT

I found my human body a definite disadvantage in watching the tidepools, especially at hand-lens distance. Not only had I to lie flat, but slanted downward, and my circulation obeyed gravity long before there was any adaptation to my new posture. When I tried to slither down to a better level I usually dipped into the water of the adjoining pool. After a quarter hour in any one position, I found that no configuration of lava was an intaglio of the human form, divine or otherwise. In other fields of endeavour, results are gained with blood and tears; but much of this work materialized only through aches and pains. I found, as when squatting in the jungle, or beginning to chatter with cold five fathoms down, that here the most exciting happenings reached a climax at the same instant when tortured muscles and nerves screamed for a shift or a rest. Thanks to the physical configuration of my body handed down by New England and British ancestors, I found that I better approximated the elongate crevices of the lava, and the first one into which I moulded myself gave an intimate view of the anemone wall hangings. I am sure that I was looking at life through the eyes of a flatworm.

I had one advantage over such a platyhelminth—what I saw coming toward me reminded me of an elephant. If such a diminutive pachyderm (I must punctuate this narrative with at least occasional scientific nodes), if an elephant of this stature had a soft, mobile skin, was dominantly green and yellow, awningwise, and possessed two trunks with which he felt his way as he crept forward on his knees, he would closely resemble the good-sized nudibranch or shell-less snail which haunted this pool. The first I saw was advancing full speed, which was about an inch in fifteen seconds. This would give odds to an ordinary snail carrying full house kit. Close behind, like trainbearers, came two very young blennies, and their pace and direction shifted but little in ten minutes. Long before this, I changed their status to camp followers, for their unvarying attendance was inspired solely by the tiny bits of food stirred up by the progress of the parti-coloured elephant snail. In this they were replicas of the antbirds and army ants in the jungle, and of gulls following the plow.

As the molluscan tank rootled over the living carpet, a wide swath became visible of annoyed, shrunken, pale-green anemones, while on each side the rich emerald of undisturbed animal herbaceous borders bloomed undisturbed. My first vista of life in the Cardon tidepools might have been a normal chapter down the rabbit's hole. I canted myself up to permit some of the blood to return to my feet, and through a mist saw the volcano puffing mightily in the distance; I recalled that this was the last day of the year nineteen hundred and thirty-seven; I looked at the freighter and hoped the seaman had had his vivifying transfusion, and then slid down again into my new world.

One joy of an expedition such as this is the wholly un-expected juxtaposition of extremes of experiences. It was much later on this same day that we were sitting in the beautiful patio of Señor Palacio in Corinto, with the essence of the tropics given by palms, lush blossoms and bright-col-oured birds in cages, when there came a sudden realization of how unalien we were in one direction. It was eleven o'clock at night on the thirty-first of December, and I reached over to a radio tuned in on a Mexican night club. A slight twist and a well-known accent rang out, "Ladies and gentlemen, it is exactly midnight here in New York City and now listen to the noise in Times Square!" Since leaving San Diego and turning south, we had imperceptibly shifted so far to the eastward that only an hour's difference in time separated us from our home city.

Next morning, on the Zaca, I woke suddenly and completely at five o'clock, which was most unusual for me. Not hearing anything out of the way, I turned over and went to sleep again. Later we found that at that hour there had been a minor earthquake on shore, many people having run out of their swaying dwellings. All day Telica poured forth an unusual amount of smoke, and even Mombobombo was ejecting steam.

Throughout the next week, whenever we could spare time from the mangroves, we made trips to the tidepools, and notebooks and pads became filled with observations on the home life and the interrelationships of the poolers. These all belong to technical, ecological treatises, but the comic and human side often made us wish for time to translate them into less formidable diction.

One phase, quite new to us, I will elaborate. I set aside certain pools as inviolate, dedicated to watching, and at once from the generic term FISH there emerged personalities which almost became friends before I paid my last visit. Now and then an incoming tide would bring a stranger or take away an oldest inhabitant, but on the whole the census remained stable. Among the fishes were those of the open water, besides cave-dwellers, creepers and climbers. Little mullets formed an ever-frightened group in the center of each pool ocean, and their whole life was one great worry, uninterrupted terror, an attempt to watch for danger in every direction at once. Rarely, inspired by momentary bravery, or more likely forced by the ultimate pangs of hunger, one would dart swiftly to the nearest seaweed-draped wall, snatch a mouthful and flee back to the midst of his palpitating fellows; heart pumping, and eyes starting. What a life!

The demoiselles lived in caves, where some of them had their nests, and their sole object in life was to dart out at every fish (which had not the slightest interest in them or their eggs), drive it away a few inches and swim quickly back. Both always seemed to take it in good part, with no harm meant or received. I do not know what would have happened if one had stood its ground, or rather water, or the other had nipped. The big ones were dark brown but the smaller demoiselles were blazing blue. Abudefdufs reminded us of Bermuda with their greenish-yellow armour, silver corselets and six vertical black stripes, giving them a rank even higher than their name of sergeant-major warrants. Their Pacific relations, nicely named Nexilarius, were still more abundant in the pools, and they bore more distinctive decorations of concentric rings of pale cream.

The creepers and the climbers were our friends the gobies and blennies, always seeming more intelligent, more aware of life than other fish. As I seem to keep on saying, they recalled the quick, virile lizards in the island scrub behind us, standing or shuffling about on their limblike pelvic fins, with birdlike turns of the head and sensitive, watchful eyes. Yet it was this very extreme adaptation to life in the tidepools which forever barred them from any further advance toward dryland existence. Here they lived in diminutive watery islands, completely

168

surrounded by hot, dry lava rocks, and yet more completely excluded from hope of shift to the air itself than their more lowly relations of the sea. No possibility of fingers and toes remained within their mittened webs, although as we watched them, we saw all the adumbrations of frogs, lizards, birds and even mammals, all potentially within their personalities.

There were three or four common species of these two groups, each individual, each unfishlike. Unworthy vernacular names for them might be Banner-finned, Emerald Horse-faced, Fringe-headed, Rock-skipping, and Blue-eyed Snake Blenny. But far more sonorous are such generic handles as, *Bathygobius, Malacoctenus, Mnierpes* and *Rupiscartes.*

For a moment let us consider *Rupiscartes,* the Rock-skipping Blenny. Its head was bright green with spots and markings of rich chestnut, lines of both colours extending back along the body and merging in a dull, negative brown or mottled coat which fitted in with any background a pool might offer. At night the brilliant colours faded, and as darkness closed down *Rupiscartes* lightened, and assumed a garb of pale creamy white, blotched and banded in a wild, irregular manner with black. Nothing could be as conspicuous as the pattern of this little chap relaxed in slumber. For his daylight suit he displayed the most invisible mosaic, for his dreams he became a Pierrot in gayest plaid.

Another blenny had a workaday mask of scarlet-and-gold eye, sage-green head with a purple cheek blotch and pink lips, a series of black spots around his so-called neck, and a scarlet fin-front. Yet amid the colours of the pool sides, all this merged into invisibility. At night a pigment wash of, literally, cold-cream colour, concealed all the glory of his day's costume.

If I described these little fish as seen after nine o'clock at night, or before six, no one would have recognized them. It reminded me of a famous botanist I once took to the first tropical rain forest he had ever seen. The flowers of the commonest trees were utterly strange to him until they were pressed, dried and brown, when they at once became his familiars of herbariums at home, and their names tripped off his tongue.

One point which I want to re-emphasize (for comparison overpage) was the wonderful resemblance of these small fish to their surroundings. A pair of gobies clinging to the anemone tapestry were, in truth, no gobies at all to our eyes until one of them shifted his position; a slope of greens and grays and browns was wholly barren of life until a rolling scarlet eye revealed a group of three exquisitely patterned little blennies. And their Mother Nature had taught them the infinite value of stillness, for, with care, one could almost touch them before they shifted. But when the shift came, the human eye recorded it only twice, once before it began and again, within the wink of an eye, the new position. What passed between was not even a blur. In the larger pools, with four or five feet of water, were scale models of what my helmet showed fathoms down off shore; lovely lavender sea fans and pencil plumes, all in height gauged to inches instead of feet. This sketchy account outlines the pools as we saw them day after day. Then I decided to try something which I had long wanted to do, which I have adumbrated in the preceding paragraphs.

At nine o'clock in the evening of the fifth of January, we all set out armed with flashlights for the tidepools on Isla

Cardon. The stars were out but it was a very dark night and the blinking lighthouse and the two entrance buoys shone brilliantly. We tied up to the old, rickety wharf, which seemed to lose a board a day, lighted our flares and started across the island. The clumps of tall, dead grass stood up in all directions, white and ghostly, and the last land-sound startled us all, as with a hoarse *paráuque!* a tropical nighthawk rose from our path.

The roar of the breakers grew louder, and I suddenly realized the first effect of darkness. Never on any of our former visits had we been aware of the sound of the ocean. We always took it for granted, and the sight of the curving green swells always dominated and muffled the sound-approaches to our conscious brain. We each had a flash and needed it, for the shifting shadows on the irregularly piled rocks made every step problematical. It was early ebbing tide, with at least three-fifths still up. The upper section of the shore sloped so gradually, however, that the water was already well down below the larger pools which we had been studying. The rocks were still wet, another nocturnal difference. In the blazing heat of day, the lava dried almost with the last wave splash. Now, with no evaporation, with constant dew, the rocks were as slippery as ice. The first thing I noticed in walking about was the presence everywhere of chitons or coat-of-mail shells. During the day, both above and below water line, they were jammed into narrow crevices, often with their curved shells touching the roof so that there was no way of prying them loose. Here the entire fraternity of hundreds were scattered over all the damp upper surfaces, well above the reach of any spray. Lowly as they are, and completely armadillo coated, they could detect the presence of light. When I allowed only the faintest penumbra of the illuminated circle to touch them, I could see they were traveling along in their slow, meandering, steady, snail-like manner, but the impact of the full glare brought them to a stop, and they did not again move until I removed the annoying rays. The giant grapsus crabs, impossible of approach in the daytime, were also wandering sleepily about, and they paid no attention to the light. I could reach down and pick them up, or if I merely touched the shell they moved away slowly. When thoroughly alarmed they merely rushed off blindly a few feet and waited further developments. What hunting this night would make for any cancrivorous bird or animal! Only the urchins, sealed forever in their individual caves, and the barnacles, soldered eternally to the lava, were unchanged by the darkness.

When I reached one of the best pools, well over toward the northwestern headland, I squatted, and snapped off the flash. The instant eclipse of my small circle of light let the omnipresent blackness strike me with almost a sentient impact. I had never before sensed the shift from concentrated illumination to complete night so instantly. And the moment I sat in darkness, the roar of the surf a few yards away became dominant again. Only the indirect, occasional, faint flare of the lighthouse well behind me broke the general darkness and this had the effect only of casual, distant lightning. I knew that within a few miles volcanoes were pouring forth their fumes, that at any moment the very earth beneath my feet might quiver and tremble; this afternoon, well on into the dry season though we were, I had felt drops of rain on my

172

face. Later a rainbow showed through the dust, an abrupt vertical section with no hint of a curve—*arc'iris*, as the natives felicitously called it. And now I flashed my light into the pool and found no lessening in the strange happenings of the day. I was in a totally new country, a pool whose fish were wholly alien.

Pool after pool drew exclamations from us. We separated and our individual lights could be seen fireflying here and there over the rocky shore. From each in turn would come surprised calls, or summons for aid in identification. For the fish were all like an unknown fauna, and emphasized the imperfections of our scientific descriptions. Death and preservation usually dimmed living, daylight patterns and colours, or obliterated them altogether. But here were the same individual fish which we had been studying a few hours earlier and for the better part of a week, all changed and altered, some beyond recognition.

Although the sleeping positions of fish were more familiar to me than to the others, yet I had forgotten that slumber could be so sound with these staring-eyed, lidless, aquatic little beings. The confusing mottling and spotting of the red-eyed blennies in the daylight, had given place to successive broad bands of dark brown, and pale colours of several shades. I had to look again and again at the sergeant-majors before I could believe that they were my old friends. The change in all was toward darkness, unlike many other species whose scaly pajamas tended toward the light colours. All silver and golden yellow were gone and the black bands had become a beautiful clear green. The fins were bright cerulean, and in two which seemed very sound asleep the head was pale blue,

173

with an appearance of transparency beneath the surface pigment. Some of these sergeants were almost horizontal, leaning far over against a seaweed-covered rock, while others were dreaming stiffly erect, braced by all their fins and quite insensitive to touch of hand or net. When carefully lifted in the net and turned on one side, there was no protest. Not until the fish was clear of the water did there result a wild thrashing and an equally instantaneous shift from dark body colour to the normal tri-coloured livery. We could imagine the dazed fish saying not only "Where am I!" but "Who am I!"

One pool was still connected with occasional inrushes of water from the last receding waves, and here were fish, which, in spite of the moving surge, had assumed slumber patterns much like wholly unrelated parrotfish. These were resting on the bottom, gently rocked back and forth by the currents without showing any signs of waking. A pair of sergeants near by had jammed themselves into narrow cracks, so that they slept motionless with bits of seaweed drifting past and over the insensitive armour of scales. I made careful notes on a wholly new species of fish which apparently had drifted in from the ocean on the afternoon tide. At last I frightened it into wakefulness and before my eyes the chestnut and spots of pale yellow dissolved, and in their place was the camouflaged mosaic of an old blenny friend.

With the invertebrates, activity was the rule at night, with serpent starfish daring to crawl about in full view, flowerworms expanded their fullest, their delicate colours visible only under the rays of my flash. As for the anemone lining of the pools, they were opened to the utmost limit, with no trace of the sand and shell blanket which had been drawn back

174

18. Bay of Fonseca. We watch a Fumerole, strange symbol of the primitive planet. Dense steam bubbles up through boulders of ancient lava.

and down out of sight, ready to be pulled over their heads at the first hint of day with its dangers. When I clicked off my light for the last time, I looked back over the wide expanse, listened to the boom of the breakers along the rim of low tide, and thought of the sleep and wakefulness, of the tragedies, deaths and births going on in a hundred of these small landlocked bits of ocean. My notebooks were full, and I felt that Corinto and Cardon had given of their best.

19. *Portières of Mangroves.* These roots walk slowly seaward, ever making new land for the continent.

CHAPTER XVI

PAPAGAYO PARADISE

ON the seventh of January we left Corinto and sailed into a sunset of orange and gold, over a mirror sea. A few hours later and we could not stay in our bunks, nor walk upright. All the next day we plowed into huge, choppy waves driven by a Force Eight, full gale of wind, under a cloudless sky with warm sunlight pouring down upon us. It was one of the dreaded Papagayos which siphons through the sierra gap made by Lake Nicaragua. After sloshing up and down for most of the day and gaining about one knot an hour, we put up two sails and fled back toward Corinto, later turning south in the partial protection of the coast. In the midst of it all, a frigatebird hung nonchalantly for ten minutes close over the masthead, and once a flock of phalaropes hurtled past, in and out of the spume. They could not have alighted and lived for a second. Just before sunset, thousands of dolphins spread over a half mile area, leaped and twisted in mid-air with utmost joy of life. What a pity these creatures are dumb; how wonderfully they would shout and sing in their bath!

Far to the north we caught a glimpse of Mombobombo quietly smoking, and then we entered the little bay of San Juan del Sur. Lack of lee gave the Papagayo full control, and as I found to my cost, the human body was everywhere at the mercy of the heavy surf. We defeated the eternal wind only by taking the gasolina twenty-three miles up and over the mountains to Lake Nicaragua. This equipage consisted of a motor-driven handcar with two wide seats, each holding four persons. It was an experience of the first water, tearing along over the narrow-gauge, around corners, through cuts and across deep arroyos, when we fully expected two of the wheels to be lifted clear of the rails, one after the other. At last we persuaded the driver that we were more interested in *pájaros, flores* and *mariposas* than in breaking speed records. The jungle was the best we had seen thus far, and our eyes were gladdened by hawks, anis, jays, orchids and quantities of butterflies.

At San Jorje on the shore of the great lake, the wind again dominated everything. Line after line of rollers and breakers tore the muddy water to shreds; pigs were rooting by the dozen in the black, mudlike, lava sand; native women strove to scrub more dirt out of their washing than the water redeposited; cormorants dived fishlessly into the opaque waves, while over all two great volcanoes had their smoke whipped about their shoulders. Damp and chilled, we took refuge in what resembled a medieval pub, and had a delicious lunch of beef and beer. We innocently bought some very beautiful Mayan bowls and figures, only to have them confiscated by the custom people when we returned to the yacht. Two of the loveliest we had wrapped for safe carrying in my sweater and these remain as the sole comforting relics of one of our less happy bays.

The Papagayo made us feel like wee, cowerin' beasties who lurked under stones and dared only dart from one shelter to another. For once I appreciated the old-fashioned maps which had personified cherubs and devils blowing, with distended cheeks, the good and the evil winds.

We were blown lustily out of San Juan del Sur and into the Bay of Santa Elena, which is the first notch in the coast of Costa Rica, heading for a baylet in its side known prosaically but officially as Port Parker, with the more pleasant native title of El Canelo, or Cinnamon Bay. After the hours of fierce buffeting it looked to us like the fabled Isles of Spice. In fact, it proved to be one of the loveliest places of Earth, bounded by mountains which mitigated the force of the wind, roughly circular, about a mile across, with heavy jungle on the nearer slopes. The higher ranges to the north rose to grass and rocky heights, the trees dying out in straggling pioneers.

There may be more diversified regions, but for its size I have never seen its equal in this respect. The greatest drawback was the overlapping of distinct areas, the three-ringed circus of interest of the wild life of sea, shore and jungle.

This is a bay where I should like to spend a full year, through all the seasons, watching the shift and change under water, along the shore, in mangroves, palm and thorn forest and upland grass meadows. One of our first trips took us up through lush mangroves, the tide carrying us along ever-narrowing channels, until we pushed our way by hand into ultimate water paths, flushing curlews, bitterns, herons and kingfishers. Dry land appeared and we climbed up into an enchanted forest or rather park of lofty trees where bands of spider monkeys swung by their tails, apparently exchanging pointed remarks on how queer human beings looked upside down. One lot of three females were all carrying babies, and in all, the pram method was identical. The baby had its tail tightly wrapped around the base of its mother's tail, as it lay on her back, with its little arms around her mid-body, gripping the hair on the lower sides. The hind legs lay straight out behind, with the black soles up, dangling close to the haunch of the mother. In this way the limbs and tail of the parent were quite free, and the baby safe from any sudden danger of being crushed when the mother dropped, from one branch or tree to another with widespread limbs. When the parents sat down and looked at us, the little chaps would pull themselves up, and their black faces peered at us alongside that of their mummy.

Here I observed what later became a common occurrence, that all the members of the band followed one another, and took exactly the same path through the trees. Each took hold of the identical same part of the same branch as the one ahead, leaped free at the same spot, and used the hands at the same place. Arboreal safari for spider monkeys is as fixed as a well-worn trail through thick undergrowth.

The grass, the meandering streams, the enormous, widespreading trees might all have been in an English park, instead of a Pacific wilderness of Costa Rica. But a pair of loud-voiced macaws and the swooping flight of trogons, together with the fresh tracks of tapirs, refocused our latitude. Following the stream we came to more open country with deep, sandy cuts and piles of dry logs and debris, showing the terrific power of the water in the rains. The logs were now covered with orchids in flower and a swarm of butterflies and equally brilliant lizards. I watched three very different butterflies alight on a mighty prostrate log, and all, at the same moment, vanished. The first invariably lit in the midst of

179

foliage, and its patterned network of brown and black lines made it a leaf among leaves; a morpho dazzled the eye with its blazing blue, but when its feet touched the bark, the wings snapped together and the eye, still blue conscious, lost the insect completely. The third was a medley of bluish white and gray, and swooped swiftly to the bark, becoming on the instant only another flake, with the wings pressed flat, so that not a hint of tell-tale shadow should escape. I greeted my very special *Junonia coenia*, and watched a five-inch jungle dragon-fly float slowly past, with its greenish yellow spots apparently pinwheeling through the air in dizzy spirals.

A quarter mile farther and the stream abruptly sank into the sand, and facing us were seven large and capable look-ing bulls. For a moment all watched us with outstretched muzzles, and my heart almost stopped, because from past experiences in the Malay States and India I am more afraid of sladangs and water buffalo than any other living creature. But after what seemed hours, these turned about and with the dainty, mincing trot of wild cattle, they left the arroyo. From time to time the stream put forth a pool and then ducked out of sight again, and these isolated bits of water, although as nearly fresh as might be, contained gobies, pipe-fish, clingfish and mullets.

Another day we landed on the opposite shore, frightening vultures from the carcass of a fourteen-foot crocodile. Around and beneath it were hundreds upon hundreds of hermit crabs, their shells clashing and tinkling pleasantly as they pushed and climbed upon the horrid feast. Above the beach line we cut and crawled through solid thickets, with bitterns and small crocs for audience, and once a tapir sloshed in person

180

through the mud to some lair unreachable by us. We climbed through bull's-horn thorn bushes, each thorn with a cohort of fire ants. To an observer our actions could have been only comic, as we skirted gingerly each innocuous-looking bush, and politely lifted aside every branch so as not to awaken the concealed ants.

We climbed and climbed until we entered upland meadows, and suddenly six cowboys rode across our path, herding wild horses, en route to a distant ranchero. Up and along sharp ridges we went on, following vague trails which, as in the Himalayas, always ran along the very crests. The bay came into view with the Zaca at anchor; the distant Pacific breakers, volcanoes with their tops swathed in cloud, and as we looked down, a pair of macaws flew past, their backs, tails and wings ablaze with scarlet, blue and yellow. Always overhead swung the zopilotes, the watchful, hopeful, graceful vultures, and still higher, mere motes against the blue, frigatebirds observed the whole world stretched out beneath them. Throughout all this day the Papagayo had miraculously died down. Only a soft breeze blew, although we could see cats'-paws stepping across the water, and far away a waterspout pirouetted as it drifted.

The hardest collecting at El Canelo was along a coral isthmus, near the outer end of the bay, an isthmus which connected the mainland with a single, gigantic rocky islet. At low tide there was never less than a foot of water over the coral, yet we were able to scatter our derris-root poison to windward, and then collect frantically as the slow current carried half stupefied octopi, worms and all manner of strange fish toward us. Papagayo, with Force Three, never let up a moment and when the tide and waves threatened to wash us out to sea, we were staggering with weariness, completely salt-encrusted, but happy with pailfuls of rare, brilliant eels and interesting young stages of angelfish, and even baby sharks and rays. The coral itself defeated us until, one morning, I pushed a full stick of dynamite as far down as possible. We all took what shelter we could find behind most inadequately small boulders, and detonated it. The geyser which rose high in air was filled with coral, the wind gave it impetus, and for many seconds we were cruelly bombed by sharp pieces. But the bruises were worth while, for this method routed out fish which had so far defied all our efforts. Long after we returned to the *Zaca* we found ourselves instinctively bracing against the blasts which had harassed us all day, giving our muscles no respite.

The value of a variety of methods in studying the fishes of these bays was shown by a comparison of tidepooling, seining, and bong-bonging (*i.e.*, dynamiting) in the course of one-half of one day. In the tidepools we took 65 fish of 6 species; in seining we hauled 416 fish of 17 kinds; in bong-bonging 186 fish yielded 15 species. But of these 36 different species of fish, taken in three ways, only 2 were duplicated, so unlike were the results of the several methods.

We had come to this bay to learn what we could of its fishes, and we had captured a splendid lot, from fresh-water mullet and clingfish out of isolated pools, a mile up a dry arroyo, to wholly new frogfish from the depths of the outer coral reefs. On the morning of the eighteenth of January I landed on East Beach (*Zaca* nomenclature), a beach of pebbles, shady trees and hermit crabs, and settled for a careful survey of the bay. I knew there were schools of fry everywhere; we had bong-bonged with small caps and netted thousands. But what was still a mystery was the hosts of fry-eaters, fish about a foot in length which leaped in every direction, but which thus far had evaded all efforts at capture. Now and then one jumped wholly out of the water, and I hoped to be able to catch a clear glimpse of it through glasses. In the space of two hours of intermittent watching, I had three definite chances, although the necessity for instantaneous refocusing one's eyes as the silvery form appeared for a moment through the binoculars was the devil's own trouble. But something more than deliberate recognition registered, and I knew for certain that the fry-eaters of Port Parker were cousins of bonefish and tarpon, fish of solid silver, with the silliest name in fishdom—Tenpounders! And with them were several small jacks whose leaps gave me the chance of naming them a hundred yards away. This provided the facts I wanted, and showed that by patience we could identify other species than flying-fish in mid-air. We had taken both fish in the vicinity of the fry but their empty stomachs made them worthless proofs. A postscript to this day's observations was that two days later, after my prolonged and successful vigil, we seined both species bursting with great meals of the selfsame fry.

A second problem was the succession of fish advancing in from the sea with each tide; which came first, and why. This was easier, for from a mangrove perch, looking down into the clear water throughout several tides, I got exactly what I wanted.

The phrase "intermittent watching" which I have used is only too real. As a scientist, I suffer from the limitations of generalities, with all the faults and unspeakable joys of the older naturalists. Until I was allowed to possess a gun I was botanist and entomologist of sorts; then I became ornithologist for the greater part of my life, and in the last decade I have turned ichthyologist. These are all lip-services however, for the underlying urge is to glimpse some small, clear gleam in the workings of evolution in some sub-sub-division of an insignificant bypath of animal life and development. So it was that in the intervals between actually straining every effort to solve the day's two fish problems, I was acutely conscious of the general life of this lovely bay.

My two assistants had left me, one on a sketching assignment, and the other to delve into the intimate life of the fiddler crabs among the mud flats farther along the shore. I settled down between two giant black mangrove trees, one of which was hollow and wind- and age-worn. I made camp by opening my dispatch case of glasses, notebooks and vials, scooped two holes in the sand for my heels and sat down on a life preserver filched from the boat. This precaution was out of respect for the bête rouge, those infinitesimal mites which seem to be among the most successful of living creatures, sustained by the ultimate Nth power hope of being able to feast upon a human being before they die. I have found them equally enthusiastic on the tennis courts of Virginia as in the tropical jungles of British Guiana, and here on the shores of the Pacific they teemed, from the grass of the upland meadows to the very jetsam of high-tide line.

As my job today was static, I allowed myself the luxury of two pairs of glasses, my smallest Number Threes for near-by use and quick identification, and the powerful Number Twelves, which required knee-rest, for distance. In addition to my two grand mangroves was a third, a whitened, dead tree. Hardly had I taken my seat when a sonorous swish of wings drew my eyes upward and out flew a great blue heron, whose spindly frame and immobility had up to this moment made him one with the tree. As I looked, two black hawks flew into the same tree, the common white-banded black species. They were handsome birds and peered at me fearlessly, uttering pleasantly quavering hawk notes. An interesting thing about birds of prey is the possibility of prophesying the diet of a species from its psychological reaction to human beings. At one end are the vultures which are almost completely fearless. At the other are the fierce falcons and eagles, who pursue and kill their prey, diving after the strongest and swiftest creatures they can manage. These black hawks have the noble facies of gerfalcons, but their all too tameness hints that, gastronomically, they are among the ignoble raptores, satisfied at the most with small lizards, but usually content with grasshoppers, snails, crabs and even dead fish. There is nothing vulturine in their mien, but their ease in the presence of mankind is a certain proof that no black hawk ever struck down a flying duck, or any bird near its own weight. By the same token, bald eagles are far less wild than are golden eagles.

After the hawks had fled I had several moments of absolute quiet. Then a familiar sound focused my senses on the shore, where a spotted sandpiper was watching me, teetering with polite inquiry, but considering me too slight a danger to interrupt for long its feeding. No matter how strange the locality, in spite of parrakeets screeching in the distance, first impressions dominate later experiences, and the *peep-sweet* of this little shorebird was always sufficient to overlay all this tropical environment and replace it with the millpond in New England where I first saw and identified the bird. It scampered on out of sight, and presently there came a jolly cackling, a familiar-unfamiliar sound, and the sandpiper had run into a pair of scarlet-billed oyster-catchers, who were telling him impolite things in *Haemantopus* language.

Fish again absorbed me until two blurred objects on the shore came into focus with a twist of the binocular thread. A pair of sandpipers this time, one with a primary feather reversed, standing straight up from the wing and waving in the breeze. I watched them idly as they passed on, when suddenly there took place, within the small circle of the lens, a happening that brought me to breathless attention. The little chap with the half-moulted feather was suddenly knocked off his feet into a fluttering heap. Discarding the glass, I saw the whole tragedy clearly. A black log, stranded by the water's edge, had suddenly come to life, shifting from dead vegetable to living animal, and with a single, unbelievably swift, sideways flick had knocked the sandpiper over. As I looked, the head turned, the jaws opened, and a four-foot crocodile sank from sight with the pitiful fluff of feathers. I watched the rising stream of bubbles, I listened to the agonizing *peeeep-peeeep!* of the other bird and the shrieking cackles of the oyster-catchers until all were lost in the distance. The only remaining proof of what my eyes had seen was that there remained only one instead of two logs. I immediately focused on the second to make certain it was what it appeared to be. During the past two days I had watched small crocodiles floating past, but the movement plus the two bulging eyes iden-

186

tified them at once. This stranded individual had completely fooled two sandpipers and myself.

The only bird sound from the jungle behind me was a resonant double-note, repeated at long intervals, and occasionally answered in the distance two notes higher. These were telegraph tom-toms of great, black and white ivory-billed woodpeckers. They had at least four drums, hollowed by lightning and seasoned by sun and rain. These rat-tat-tats kept up a pleasant, subdued, antiphonal obligato throughout all the afternoon, soon, like Dunsany's cricket, merging into the silence.

A medley of voices arose not long after the sandpiper tragedy, and as it did not die down, I walked quietly along the inland trail. Just beyond the uprooted base of a giant tree, I saw the flock of birds and simultaneously felt a sharp bite on my ankle. I had stepped into the line of march of army ants, and as instantly I stepped out again. The reason for the flock now became apparent; they were the camp-following vanguard feeding on the insects which crept, ran, hopped or flew to escape their dreaded enemy. I found a convenient dead branch and as quietly as possible drew it back and forth across the trail of the ants. I knew that this would so infuriate them that they would deploy in search of the creature which dared disturb them, and this would keep them, and consequently the birds, in the same place for some time. I sought safety and settled to watch. There were four kinds of antbirds and a surprising lot of orioles. Three troupials fluttered about after insects, alternating satisfied swallows with clusters of liquid notes. A black-throated oriole flew down close to me, and then suddenly I was glad to see a friend from home, a

Baltimore oriole among these alien surroundings. What tales, migrants such as this and the sandpipers had to tell their nestlings! No wonder each season's brood is so anxious to set out on its autumnal, austral voyage of discovery!

Finally, six rich rufous beauties scaled down to the ant-driven harvest—rufous cuckoos. They measured more than a half yard over all, and their exciting loveliness of plumage, with the long, trailing, white-tipped tail made them most conspicuous birds. Their unusual size and general colouration always recalled female curassows. Yet the latter, with all their strength and stout beaks, are the most timorous of jungle birds, whereas these cuckoos, with beak and claws of the weakest, flaunt their brightness with utmost carelessness. They must have some way, of which we are wholly ignorant, of escaping the abundant hawks. They saw me at once but showed only polite curiosity, now and then uttering their low, soft snarl, which is in no sense a snarl, but lacks any adequate expression in the English tongue. They flew gently, gliding whenever possible, and fed gently, daintily selecting small morsels with no sense of hunger or haste, but somewhat reluctantly, like the oyster-eating Carpenter.

I was squatting quite motionless, and comfortable, having only, now and then, to wink. So one cuckoo relegated me to the background of innocuous growths, and, alighting on a partly bare branch, proceeded to take a sun bath. The plumage is so soft and silky that it would seem as if the water or dust bath to which most birds are addicted would leave it with permanently bedraggled feathers. This sun bathing was as elaborate as it has become among human beings, but was infinitely more artistic and pleasing to observe. The bird first sat still and looked in all directions, complimenting me by concentrating on the branches overhead and the sky. It suddenly struck a pose, legs apart, leaning backward, slanting the great tail and spreading it until it formed a gorgeous open, feathered fan, curved so that the white tips showed from both sides. The wing on the slanted side followed, and was expanded until, like the argus pheasant, it presented a flattened plaque. Always the eye of the bird played back and forth across the sky; at least at such a period of toilet-making a realization of possible danger was evident.

Slowly the feathers of the head and neck were raised (through my lenses I could distinguish every separate plume), until all beauty of colour was lost, and the plaque acquired the appearance of moth-eaten plumage long neglected in some dusty attic. After a few minutes the bird began to pant, and to general dishevelment was added the impression of acute physical torture. Ten minutes, and all muscles relaxed, and the bird began to pick and preen its plumage, the intensive efforts hinting that ticks and bête rouge may afflict *Piaya cayana* as well as *Homo sapiens*. Not until a second bath was enjoyed by the other wing, with the tail reslanted, did the bird shake its whole being, wipe its beak on the branch and fly up into a mass of lavender Flowers of Cortez.

As I looked down, preparing to shift my stiff, tightly flexed limbs, I saw that a small spiny-bodied spider had stretched three strands of suspension cable from knee to knee, and I felt that I had really entered into the feeling of the jungle.

On my return to the shore, I once more settled down to a final hour of writing, when a tantalizing wheezy note arose from the tree overhead. I had to determine whether it was insect or bird, and my eye went at once to what looked like a small duck perched in a crotch. This spelled no sense whatever, yet amid the shadows of the foliage I could see bill, eye and the head drawn close to the back. Two feet farther up I was startled to see the brilliant and unmistakable tail loop of a boa constrictor, and now I followed it down to the small duck and the scales fell from my eyes and for the life of me I could not regain the anatine illusion; there was no duck, there had been no duck; only three loops of a beautifully coloured serpent. In fact, the glasses showed that from the tangled mass of loops there projected two heads, one much larger than the other. I needed a boa for comparison with a strangely patterned specimen we had caught a few days before. A second would decide whether this unusual colouration was of specific or only individual significance.

The snake was twenty feet above me, on a dead branch which would not sustain my weight for a moment. I cut a long, forked stick and began to jiggle him, which made him only grip the tighter. He began to creep slowly up the branch, when I got a good purchase with a recurved crook, and swinging on it, broke the whole branch, and down came a rain of rotten wood, debris, dust and more than seven feet of snake. Fearing it would escape if it touched the ground, I blindly clutched at it in mid-air, and no lifelong-trained juggler could have done it better, for my fingers closed firmly around the neck just behind the head. Like all his kind, he gaped widely, uttering hiss after hiss, showing every needle tooth and an enormous expanse of dead white gullet, all the time trying with every muscle to coil and twist free. Then he gave up, and, as boas are real gentlemen, he shrugged whatever pass

190

20. *Enchanted Island, Corinto. The beach is drifted high with windrows of olive shells.*

for serpentine shoulders, and resigned himself to what might come. From this moment on, there was no visible resentment, or active attempt at escape. The coils came slowly up and around my hand and arm, and when I had cleared the dirt from my eyes, I did not have to shift my grip a single inch.

I looked longingly up at the second boa, beautifully marked and at least twelve feet in length, but saw no way of getting him as he climbed to the very summit of the tree. An hour later when I again looked, he had vanished, although he must have reached out over a four-foot interval of thin air between the dead tree and the nearest live one.

Returning to my seat I found neither string nor bag nor container, so that I had to shift my hold to the left hand to continue note writing with the right. My foot rested gently on his tail on the sand, because with all his folds in a double lock on my wrist, he was able to stop the blood supply, and the hand ached too much to keep a tight grip. As it was, I had to stop writing every ten minutes, shift hands, and exercise to restore circulation. As the lowering sun struck his armour, he was one of the most beautiful things in the world, each scale giving off blue and green fire-opal reflections. Like the jumbled mass of leaf patterns and leaf shadows scattered along his body, his very eyes, lidless and unwinking, were also mottled with gray and brown, divided equally, while the vertical slit of visual connection with the outside world was almost invisible. (Plate 24.)

During one of the hand-to-hand shifts I happened to look out over the bay, and floating past was a pair of huge sea turtles, clasped in the awkward embrace of chelonian affection. I focused my glasses and perceived that it was a most

191

21. *Olivella Shells*. A close-up of the billions scattered over the shore, never any two exactly alike.

active amorous episode, for not only were they excitedly clambering over and around one another, but both were revolving as they drifted past. First one arched back would emerge decorated with clusters of barnacles, and then the other, gay with waving strands of emerald seaweed. Which sex flaunted the weed, and which had acquired the barnacle insignia will never be known. This afternoon was rapidly becoming dominantly a reptilian one.

When I withdrew my eyes from the binoculars, I found myself securely handcuffed by two loops of boa, one of which was a figure eight. I saw the boatmen approaching, and did not untwine the snake until they had had full benefit of what to them seemed an incredibly terrible situation. They were strong, brave, able seamen, but I think if it came to a choice of unwinding the coils with their own hands they would have left me marooned forever on the beach!

Subsequently the colour comparison was made, the boa housed overnight on the yacht, and next day I set him free on the exact spot on which he would have fallen from the tree. He gathered himself together, watched me calmly, and finally, with exploratory flickering of his tongue, slowly and with dignity made his way into a tangle of underbrush. From the opposite side I watched him glide smoothly along. Before he had passed from my actual field of vision, he vanished suddenly, from my inability to disentangle him from his surroundings.

The boa constrictor of East Beach had entered and had left my life; he none the worse, and I with added knowledge and respect for him and his race.

CHAPTER XVII

THE BAY OF SEA SNAKES

WE left Port Parker at dawn and raced for the next bay, beating the slowly rising Papagayo by a gust. This was Murcielago, or the Bay of the Bats. It was large, only partly protected, and the pounding surf kept us well off, our small rowboat rocking madly on the passing swells. We did not land and we left after half a day, yet memory still holds vivid several happenings.

We were water-glassing and drifting slowly along at high noon, when, on peering suddenly up out of my bucket, I saw a tapir standing broadside on, close to the water's edge. He looked as big as an elephant, flicked his ears, waggled his nose at us, waded through some shallows and vanished.

Hardly had he disappeared when, without any warning, a short distance astern, where we had just passed, an enormous wave suddenly made up in mid-water, from nothing, curving at least twelve feet into the air, and crashing shoreward with a terrific roar. It was fifty yards or more from the breakers along the shore, its extent was not more than fifty feet, and it was preceded and followed by perfect calm. It left us gasping. If we had not drifted beyond its path we should have been smashed into splinters. Unless it was due to some inconceivably localized bottom disturbance, we had no explanation.

The only bats we saw here were sea-bats, giant rays or sea-

193

devilettes, belonging to our newly named species, *lucasana*. They appeared by the dozen, as suddenly as the tapir and the wave, and leaped high into the air in pairs, their great wing-fins flapping as they shook themselves and somersaulted, a futile attempt at abortive flight.

Seining was impossible, dredging barren, and so we left after lunch and in a few hours were in Potrero Grande. On the way I looked up this name in a Spanish dictionary, and found that it meant "a surgeon who cures ruptures." The second definition was more possible, "a cattle farm." But at Potrero Grande not only were there no surgeons or farms but few or no opportunities for collecting and studying wild life. A seining party was rewarded with a haul of 4335 thread herrings, of which we returned 4333 to their watery home. With them, however, was a real prize in the form of ten *Dixonina*, which is one way of indicating a species of ladyfish or bonefish with an elongated filamentous element in the dorsal fin, like that of the tarpon. This was hitherto known from only two specimens, so Potrero Grande acquired a bit of merit.

The next bay was Culebra, which we reached at noon on the twenty-fourth of January. The aptness would have been perfect if its name had been *Culebra del Mar*, for we found it to be really a bay of sea snakes. Papagayo was also in full possession and our utmost efforts to buck the wind and sea and accomplish reasonably good work were all but unavailing. For example, we laboured for a full morning in three or four feet of water, over coral heads in a choppy sea. A moment's lull would show some treasure almost at our very feet, and with great exertion we would occasionally retrieve it only to have it dashed out of our hands or washed out of our collecting pails by the smashing masses of water. One dead pinna or Spanish oyster showed a glint of bright colour within the valves, and this I threw bodily into the pitching pram, and later found two yellow, red and brown eels, both new, beneath the floor boards.

Once, Jocelyn spied a box crab larger than any ever recorded, but the roughness of the surface, and the buoyancy of the human body, reversing and remaining in reverse, in four feet of rough salt water, were all in favor of the escape of the crab. Through the water-glass from the boat, we later saw a yard-long eel, with a thick, blunt head, finless as far as we could see, painted with an amazing pattern of hundreds upon hundreds of very narrow golden, black and greenish-white concentric rings, from snout to tail-tip. Although only five feet beneath our keel, it might just as well have been five miles, for anything we could do about it. We watched the prize wind slowly out of sight, and cursed our aquatic limitations. I had the same sensation of helpless misery as when some unknown, unnamed abyssal fish swam tantalizingly close to the bathysphere window.

A chattering disturbed my mental anguish, and looking over the gunwale of the drifting boat I saw we were close to a branch overhanging the water, and near the tip were two black capuchin monkeys, black with yellowish-white face, cheeks and chest. They twittered pleasantly, paying little attention to us until I said something to them in capuchin language. It was a sound which always caused my pet monkey Chiriqui to answer in kind, but in the dialect of this Culebra clan it apparently meant something disturbing, for they stared hard, stuffing their cheeks with flower petals as they looked, and then made off.

Finally, in desperation, we rowed into the inadequate lee of a ledge of rocks, and set off a stick of explosive. The result was unusual, because there seemed to be only a single species of fish affected, about two hundred chunky-looking, striped grunts. Before we had fired the cap we had noticed a lone frigatebird high in air, but in five minutes after the first dead fish appeared on the surface there must have been one hundred birds in a dense cloud close about us. They showed no fear but swooped down to within a few feet. The fish were about all they could lift, as they were from six to eight inches and heavy in proportion. When they caught a fish by the tail they rose some distance into the air, and if lucky enough to avoid the attacks of their friends, they would drop the fish with no upward toss, and instantly sink faster than their prey, seize it daintily by the head, rise again and swallow it. It was the superlative in flight.

Every day at Culebra opened the same. At seven o'clock when we were at breakfast on deck there was no breeze, not a cloud in sight; the bay was a mirror. Then a few wisps appeared over the distant mountains to the northeast, and more came in sight, scudding fast. They never ceased after this, although the sky might not be wholly overclouded until afternoon. By seven-thirty a ripple marred the water and the first breeze began, soon followed by strong and irregular gusts. And so the Papagayo got down to its daily work of blocking the labours of visiting scientists.

At about nine in the evening I went on deck and found the sky clear with the wind blowing in light to strong gusts.

The water showed numerous sparks of green phosphorescence, not so abundant but what they might have been the reflections of the more brilliant stars. Whatever creature swam near the yacht instantly caught fire and every part of its body was etched in flame. It was possible to identify fish and jellies. Four sea snakes which undulated past were literally fiery serpents, but all headless, because this portion was reared above the surface in the blackness of the air.

In the dark I took a long-handled net and began to sweep in small circles as far as I could reach. The net began to glow, then actually to flame with light. When I lifted it over the rail and above the deck, the bottom meshes literally dripped and poured forth what looked like molasses of living fire. When washed into an enamel pan, a thousand sparks shone for a moment, then all quieted down into a milky fluid. The deck was splashed with pale turquoise-green paint or milk—similes kept pouring into our minds. Every spark on the deck dreened forth a stream of the emerald milk, which extended at times two inches or even three from the source.

In the light, the dish showed innumerable small, brown, active creatures; the low-power resolved them into a pure culture of ostracods, small bivalved crustaceans, all with eggs in various stages of development. We wondered about the males until we remembered that their close relatives had been bred for thirty years in a laboratory without the assistance of a male. If we impaled one on the tip of a needle, the green flare was visible even in the bright electric light. Then, if the light was turned off, the sight under the lens was like a living, moving galaxy. The source was solid, shining green, burning steadily. With every twist of the needle, curling skeins and clouds of luminous smoke which was fire, poured forth and spread over all the microscopic field, illuminating everything.

For an hour and a half, as long as we left the light on, there was no diminishing in the number of the ostracods. Billions upon billions of them passed slowly, drifting on the tide, regardless of whether there was a complete calm, or whether a squall swirled full force. It was decidedly a night of ostracods.

The first midnight in Culebra I was awakened by a terrific banging on deck and the crash of breakable things. Although the Zaca was riding steadily at anchor, I found the small boats were standing on end in a violent gale of wind, with the sky perfectly clear and the Southern Cross well up and glowing brightly. I had not felt such pressure since a hurricane on Nonsuch. The swells were high and exceedingly long so that the crests were far apart, and whenever these broke or were wind-shattered they were brilliant with lambent phosphorescence. Every member of the crew was at work, clothed or unclothed, making the boats safe. In a fortunate lull, both launches were hoisted aboard, and the engines started in case of the anchor dragging. It was Force Nine and had arisen without warning. Such tricks does the Papagayo play, even, as now, on the very southern edge of its domain. The wind slowly decreased, and one of the early morning watch excitedly reported a lion roaring on the neighboring shore, a proof that we were really working down into the true tropics, and that howling monkeys were abroad.

Sea snakes were more abundant here than we had found them anywhere, and we could have collected a hundred if we had so desired. When we left the Zaca in early morning several would invariably swim out from under the keel, and they came to every night light. The luminous attraction was slight but very apparent, and once a large yellow and black serpent made six anti-clockwise turns. I touched him with the net ring and frightened him into reverse gear, but the magnet of the light drew him back again.

I watched these snakes and experimented with them, and the result was my constant surprise at their poor swimming ability. A sea snake must support itself in water throughout its entire life, and it is provided with a flattened paddle-tail, but when frightened or pursued, it never dashes off, as would a black snake on land, or an eel in water, but dives at once. This absence of high speed is very likely connected with its venomousness, for it rarely needs to flee from any enemy. The blatant, warning colours support this theory. A rattle-snake is similarly slow of scale flight, but instead of colour, it relies on the sense of hearing to proclaim its presence.

Further study of stranded sea serpents reconfirmed my belief that these reptiles are wholly aquatic, even as to breeding. I found a number stranded in various places, and all reacted the same way. One yellow and black beauty, about eighteen inches in length, was left by the tide on a ledge of rocks near the entrance of the bay. I was working the near-by pools and watched it from time to time. It was helpless from the very first, a few minutes after the last wave lapped its rock. It struck feebly at my waving hand, but there was no attempt or apparent ability to coil first, only a slight reaching out of the head and neck. It strained and turned from side to side, but made no progress, and after two hours it showed distinct signs of distress, striving to jam its head into an adjacent crevice, and wriggling to no purpose. Less than a foot away were several deep, water-filled furrows in the rock, yet nothing in its sensory makeup told it of this fact. When I was ready to leave, the snake was dry and practically dead, so that I handled it without fear. I had similar experiences with other snakes and there was no variation. When stranded on sand, they were equally helpless, and efforts at escape were as often headed inland as back toward the water a few feet away. (Plate 23.)

From one snake netted from the Zaca, thirty-three inches long, I took five well-grown embryos, each neatly done up in a translucent, individual package, like a short sausage, within which each was folded up exactly alike. The head and the tail were uppermost, while the body beneath lay in two identical, equal coils. They averaged seven inches in length and their colour and pattern were clearly indicated. No one has ever witnessed the birth of a sea snake, but when that happens, I am sure the infant will be ushered out into salt water, and not, like a baby seal, even temporarily onto rocks or sand of the shore.

One of the strangest uses to which I have seen these snakes put, was as protection or sanctuary by small fish. When the Zaca was drifting slowly along far out at sea, with the deep nets trailing, snakes would sometimes pass directly beneath me as I lay on the farther tip of the boom-walk platform. Again and again I saw a small school of young fish swimming along in an elongated group not far beneath the reptile, exactly as their fellows took advantage of the shelter of floating logs or even large feathers. This would seem to be a risky business, for at any moment their shelter might dive and seize one of them. Several times I have found the remains of small fish in their stomachs, but I doubt if ever the capture was made by full-speed pursuit.

We explored the upper reaches of a mangrove stream, sheltered from the full wind, which twisted and turned with such effectiveness that after half a mile I found myself only a stone's throw from where we started. Taking a short cut out by way of an old trail near a slow-flowing stream, and coming out on the bay, I encountered one of the jolliest human beings I have ever met. He was filling a none-too-clean pail at a muddy puddle in the stream, a puddle only too evidently beloved of deer and tapir. He offered me a drink, "*¡bueno para beber!*" but I firmly refused. He talked steadily, and found life one huge joke, roaring at intervals at anything provided with the thinnest or the coarsest veneer of humour. He watched me chase and capture a butterfly, and this was to him sheer comedy, the high-light joke of the day.

He called his wife, shy but as smiling as he. She was carrying a baby and gradually, closing in on us, came nine more children, all smiling, all unbelievably ragged, but healthy and good-looking, embarrassed by fewer and fewer clothes as their ages decreased. They had walked all the way from a place called Liberia, a distance of some twenty kilometers, and were soon to return, after eating a lot of sea food. It was apparently the Culebran way of going to the Riviera or taking the waters.

All of them had been digging clams and some kind of wild yam, and all seemed to think life was lots of fun. Their idea of the object of my search seemed somewhat distorted, but they too began to hunt butterflies assiduously, and one or two of the flock nibbled at the bodies, looking at me dubiously out of the corner of their eyes, and later offered me the dismembered parts. The pursuit was the thing, however, for it seemed to promise to satisfy their two greatest cravings—food and fun.

I asked where they would spend the night and the man vaguely waved his hand, somewhere hereabouts, *¡como no!* Gifts sobered them for a moment when we brought out food and Christmas leftovers from the yacht. These were something to wonder about and frown over. Such a thing had not happened before in all their lives, and at first there seemed to be an embarrassing wait to see what would be demanded in return. The evening and night were chilly, but at daybreak, through my glasses, I saw the mother taking her horde down to the water's edge and scrubbing them in relays, while they leaped and skipped along the shore. Even at that distance I could see that they were all laughing. What a family! What a life!

Toward the end of our stay we spent much time studying the inhabitants of a strip of diversified beach. In the face of the advancing tide I salvaged a great mass of mollusk egg cases, as large as my head. Seated on the sand, with my golden shell nursery on a flat rock before me, I began to analyze this attempt on the part of some snail, living in the bay, to perpetuate her race. The affair consisted of a circular lot of rosetted, involuted, flat leaves, like the petals of a rose, eighty-six in number. Each leaf was composed of at least two hundred rows or side branches, and every one of these comprised a minimum of three hundred and fifty shell sacs. The sacs were about an eighth of an inch in length.

With my hand lens, and on a flat pearly valve lined with the whitest of white nacre, I counted the contents of three of the sacs, and found one hundred and eighty-nine, one hundred and ninety, and two hundred and six embryos respectively. These were the reason for the whole contraption, and each tiny creature, most active and excited, possessed a perfect, individual shell, all to himself, simple, flat, and coiled several times.

I totted up the snail nursery; the 86 leaves, 200 rows, the 350 sacs, and the coddled 190 baby snails. Result: the parent snail had produced one billion, one hundred and thirty-seven million, seven hundred and eighty thousand infants. This fertility of a Culebra Bay mollusk seemed to have much in common with the tale of stars in the heavens.

At lunch time we found that we had food in abundance but had forgotten all utensils. The spirit of Mrs. Swiss Family Robinson descended upon us, and within a few yards we gathered a complete luncheon set; flat, mother-of-pearl oyster plates, eight inches across, deep pecten saucers and fluted limpets for cups, forks of palm spines, and knives of Noah's ark shells. Thin sheets of coconut bark matting provided adequate napery. Our improvised cutlery and crockery equaled those of the yacht in utility and far excelled them in beauty.

Like Henry the Eighth we carelessly threw our crusts and chicken bones over our shoulders, and before long a rustling drew our attention and we saw several big hermit crabs wrestling mightily over our luncheon detritus. A second glance aroused the same thought in each of us and we began to chant a paraphrase of Tweedledee's verse:

Four other Hermits followed them,
　And yet another four;
And thick and fast they came at last,
　And more, and more, and more—
All hopping through the frothy waves,
　And scrambling to the shore

only our multitudes were scrambling through the underbrush. All were headed upwind and jostling along, falling over obstacles in their eagerness, like some comically insane gold rush.

Suddenly there came to me with new vividness the incongruous part which these beautiful, pilfered houses were playing in the lives of these hermits. I saw each of them in my mind's eye as it was at first, slowly forming, layer upon layer of lime, smooth, rough, curved or spiky; rose, purple, green or ivory. Gradually it took form and architectural shape, all the time carried along by its snail owner at a solemn, dignified pace, the dwelling of an aristocratic mollusk.

At last the owner passed on; never by choice, seldom by death from old age, but usually by some tragic attack of bird, or animal, voracious fish or even by assault from some member of its own phylum. The beautiful shell became a lifeless, deserted thing, washed by the waves and sand until revivified by a passing hermit. And here about us were hundreds of these shells, their whole character changed, dancing a new, irrelevant masque, tumbling about, traveling at breathless speed compared with their former gait, all in high gear, all dignity, all sober progress gone forever. The marble château has become a night club.

Not far from the edge of the water a group of four hermit crabs showed no interest in the food, and their strange actions drew me close. Two crabs of two distinct species were attacking a third of the same kind as one of the assailants. There was something definitely the matter with the victim. The attackers held the unfortunate one down, waiting motionless until he made a move, when both leaped fiercely at him and tried to drag him from his shell. When I interfered, he fled at once in a limping, hobbling manner, and examination showed that two legs were missing, and furthermore a bad odor emanated from his shell. While I held him in my hand the others searched everywhere, and when I set him down they sprang like tigers upon him. It was rather horrible, and ultimately I threw him well out into the healing salt water of the bay.

In the midst of a session of note-writing I twice caught sight of a shark's fin not far from shore. A third time it split unexpectedly into a dozen, elongate, curved fingers and I knew that my eyes and mind had fooled me. I recognized the remains of a brown pelican which we had thrown overboard after identifying the food and preserving the skull. The carcass had drifted ashore and was now rolling over and over in the swells, exposing the tip first of one wing, then the other above water. After an hour, when I again looked, the pelican was high and dry, and had increased in size and come to life in a mass of sable incarnations. It was buried deep beneath what ultimately resolved into six and twenty black vultures.

I walked slowly past them, well down near the retreating tide, and one by one, they first ran, then hopped or kicked themselves into the wind until they had sufficient impetus for a take-off. Only three were left and these quarreled with each other with heads well within the rib chamber, for the pelican was picked clean except for skin and tendons. Most of the fighting was done by pushing alone. Holding their wrinkled heads well down, they humped their shoulders and strained and pushed mightily, for all the world like a right guard and his opponent at the moment of a center play. The unnatural thing about these birds was the silence of all this violent action; at the most there were a few, low, asthmatic hisses.

I walked straight down wind on the trio, and they all moved ahead of me, and when I ran they merely increased their speed in preference to trying to rise *with* the strong wind. Some time later I heard a guttural croak and saw that a caracara had arrived and was joining the trio of scavengers. In general appearance this bird compares favorably with hawk or eagle, but in flight, gait and appetite it could call the vulture cousin, at least. Whether because of a powerful, hooked beak, impressive carriage, or the possession of a real voice, however ill-sounding, the caracara is the superior of the vultures, and when this bird reached the pelican, the zopilotes withdrew into a disrespectful circle. A few moments of idle pecking discouraged the new arrival, and it walked away. The indecorous, hissing mob at once overran the carcass, and again the caracara approached. It seemed to think that such eagerness and gastronomic faith must have some material basis.

Later I rediscovered the caracara some distance down the beach going through a strange performance. It would compress every feather on its body, making a thin shadow of its usual self, then slowly advance and suddenly reach out a foot with widespread talons, make a quick snatch and leap back. All this I saw clearly through my binoculars, and then it was

206

22. *Poisoning a Tidepool for Rare Fish and Crabs.*

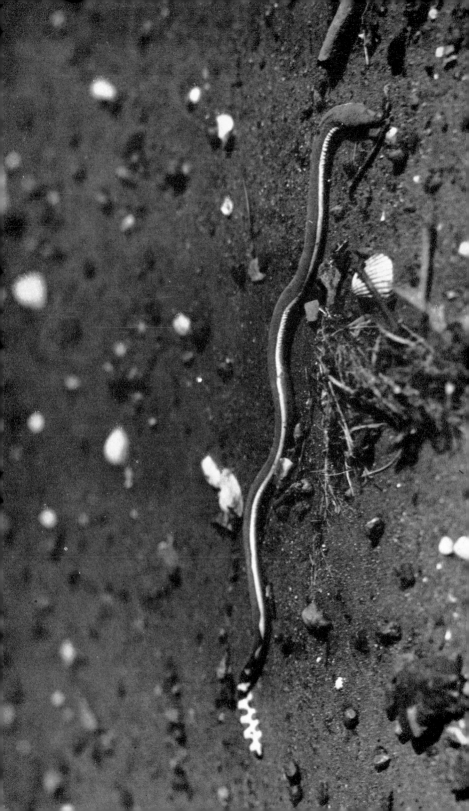

repeated with no variation three times. It was exactly the performance of a secretarybird with a snake. I walked down and found that the bird was snatching at a sea snake about two feet in length, which had been stranded by the tide. It was very much alive and struck when I annoyed it.

The single remaining black had been joined by a red-headed turkey vulture. I took up the snake on a stick, carried it to the pelican and dropped it in the midst of the carcass. When the birds returned they saw the reptile at once and their reaction was to half raise the wings in the wind, in readiness for an instant leap up and back. Both birds began to drag the bones away from the reptile, pulling together and with all their might, two working for the same purpose. Twice, when the snake made a sudden motion, the red-headed bird shifted a wing directly in front of its body, a method of defense which elsewhere I have seen only in a roadrunner. These are small happenings, but all worthy of record as facts in an ultimate better understanding of avian psychology.

Braxilito, although a pleasant word, has left, as a bay, only the slightest imprint on our memory. We anchored at three in an afternoon, and found the shore completely inaccessible because of series of pounding breakers. My notes say, "We saw horsemen, men on foot and a woman with a red skirt." That is all.

At night we had a splendid catch of young fish of many species about the light, so Station 207—light—1, keeps Braxilito on our records. Next morning we found the waves higher than ever, and forthwith put to sea.

At mid-morning we passed Cape Velas, which is said to be the southernmost limit of the Papagayo, and every one of us

207

23. *Culebra Bay.* A stranded, helpless sea snake slowly expires on the shore just above the reach of the ebbing tide.

sent up a heartfelt prayer for its truth. For almost a month and for quite one hundred and fifty miles we had been plagued by this pestilential draft. Our prayers must have been intercepted by old man Papagayo himself, for with fiendish humour, he instantly forged a Number Nine Force Squall. This, however, soon blew out and afterwards we rejoiced in light winds and calm water.

The easing of the eternal wind brought about a corresponding relaxation in my own person, and I went slowly below and to my cabin, for once with no impelling idea of something needing to be done at once. In this calm interlude of wind and mind, I flopped down and looked around my little kingdom with a possessive grin. As a matter of fact, my cabin on the Zaca is not undeserving of the personal pronoun, for in the course of three years it has been my home for almost seven months. I chose it at first because it is at the very foot of the companionway, and in hardly more than three motions I can swivel out of bed, out of the door and up the steps to the deck. The first spider monkey I saw swinging through the branches on this trip brought a fellow feeling as to motion, for with a touch on the handrail, and two successive hand grips placed at just the right distances, I can go up and down even in the roughest rolling as subconsciously as my tailed relatives do through wind-tossed branches.

Small islands and small workrooms are two reasons why I enjoy life so much on this earth, and my cabin is seven-by-nine. This, if actually true, would be disappointingly commodious, but two and one-half feet are occupied by an extra berth above and behind my own, and this is my storage room; a corner is used up as a large closet, and another corner by a chest of drawers. So my floor space is only a few inches larger than my bunk, which is as perfect a place in which to think, read, write and even to sleep as could possibly be desired.

A period of seventeen months elapsed between my first and second occupancy of the *Zaca* cabin, yet again and again I had most drastic proofs of how strongly implanted in us is automatic, instinctive memory of position and movement in space. Lack of book room led the ever-thoughtful Templeton to provide a surprise in the shape of two-foot book shelves in my cabin, beginning at shoulder height. It took about eight severe concussions before the realization of them as an obstruction when I left the cabin in a great hurry supplanted the scores of times I had made my exit before they were erected.

Many weeks had passed before I found out that I was sleeping under water. At the thought I got up and looked out. My single porthole, which must forever be sealed, was only inches above the surface when the sea was perfectly calm, and at this particular moment there was a pleasant swell and heave. As I looked out, we rolled, and the sunlit waves gave place instantly to a solid greenness which stirred up places and feelings I had almost forgotten: a window eight inches across, a blaze of light which changed to a smother of foam and sheer greenness. As I looked I seemed to be in a still smaller room, crouched down, with every part of me concentrated in intentness of vision. After three years and three months I was again in the bathysphere and the surface splash was just over as I began a descent. After this, a day seldom passed when I did not pause for a moment to watch for the greenness.

Much of the normal but wholly interesting life on board a

ship at sea passes into unnoticing subconsciousness. How terribly easy it is to let exciting little things slip past, without note, from sheer familiarity; to have the contour range of one's thoughts leveled by the insidious insistence of a mentally myopic lack of perspective; to realize that simple but vitally significant fancies and feelings are being obscured or obliterated, as they submerge beneath the opaque surface of usualness. Now and then, comparisons with land living cropped up as interesting accompaniments.

On board a yacht such as the *Zaca*, water, for many days out of port, was as little a matter of conscious concern as on land. We remembered not to waste it and that was all. One night I was awakened from sleep by a new and to me sinister sound. I sat up in my bunk and listened. We were going ahead quite silently, but rolling now and then in the trough of a swell, and with each roll there came from beneath my feet the sound of water sloshing about. Just for a moment I felt panic. The waves slapping against the side of the *Zaca* had become so accustomed a sound that it had passed into a part of the silence. But this was different and brought to mind two unpleasant experiences of the past; once the sound of water in a leaking vessel as we went full speed for shallow water, gambling buoyancy against time and barely winning, and again when I stood on the engine-room ladder of the slowly sinking *Gladisfen*, watched the water pour through the opened sea cocks and listened to its ghastly slapping against the engines and sides. And here on the *Zaca* was the selfsame sound, a delayed surge coming a little after the roll of the vessel, with a continued splashing beneath my very cabin. I was not happy, yet I knew somehow that my fears were based on sheer ignorance. I crept up the companionway and saw the calm expression of the helmsman faintly reflected in the compass light, and went back to bed.

For a day or two the faucets misbehaved. Water would come forth decorously enough for a time, then a sudden blast of air would almost dash the toothbrush from one's hand. One morning nothing, not even air, came out. To a landsman this would have been a signal to send a hurry call for a plumber, for to any "city crow" concern with water comes only when it is lacking, or produces what we smugly call *bad* weather, materializing in the form of fog, rain, snow or ice.

Synchronized with the failing faucet was the appearance of a fat little red jug at my elbow, our water ration. I well recall my first fears as to the proper distribution of this definite amount of liquid. Statistics as to the amount of gallons passing over a waterfall or through a pipe or faucet had never conveyed an iota of sense to me, and now I had no precedent to help. I wondered whether I should forego a shave as the least necessary use of the suddenly precious liquid. Teeth and mouth must come first, and I found I had used an astonishingly small amount of water. I became bolder and when I had finished shaving I found I still had half a jug left, and with this passed my initiation in water rationing.

Several times in isolated bays when water ran low and the interest of the place demanded a prolonged stay, shore parties would report the discovery of accessible fresh water. This was ordinarily absolutely taboo—a sip or drink ashore being considerably more dangerous than the percentage of risk of being bitten by a poisonous snake. But modern chemistry has changed all this. The crew would bring back a great cask filled with many gallons of water which contained all the potentialities of a quick and unpleasant death from typhoid or amoebic dysentery, and into it would be poured a little liquid guaranteed to make the water fit for drinking.

The Zaca was an enormous floating sanctuary, or a comfortable yacht, or a mere bobbing chip, according to the various points of view of an attached barnacle, myself, or a frigate-bird a mile up in the heavens. From beginning to end of both trips, except for occasional blows, we were able to eat in comfort on deck, thanks to movable canvas walls or dodgers. Thus the saloon was free to be transformed into a working, pukka laboratory, with work tables, drawers, book racks, electric lights, microscope stands, jar and vial holders. The ever-shifting and increasing containers of ill-mated squids, fish, sea snakes, butterflies, birds and bugs, in apparent confusion, were worth while if only for the varied expressions they elicited on the faces of visiting Latin-American customs and other government officials. (Plate 25.)

We often played a game of thinking the thoughts of captains of the Spanish galleons, whose wakes of old in these waters we so often disturbed by our own. We visualized the China ships coming in to Acapulco, with the crews prostrate from scurvy, and compared them with our own lime-filled lockers, and refrigerators bursting with every fruit, vegetable and perishable meat conceivable. We even wondered what Darwin would say to the changes made in collecting and study-on-the-spot since he visited the Pacific, one hundred and three years before.

Our special magic was Toshio Asaeda, who could do anything, and did it without cessation in what was literally a crack or crevice in one corner of the laboratory. He was believed to sleep there, although no one ever saw him with his eyes shut throughout all three years. He skinned birds, from albatrosses to hummers, dissected crocodiles and mounted insects; he cleaned thousands of mollusks; he photographed, developed and enlarged; he ate rarely; and all in an area of a size usually allotted to a single person in a cemetery.

I ticked off the sounds of the Zaca: The low hum of the generator, which no one ever heard until it stopped; the ship's clock (with another always slow enough for an echo); the never-to-be-forgotten whine of the deep-sea wire on the winch; and the buzzer announcing the arrival of the net itself. Rarely came the deep roar of the engines in reverse, as we anchored, preparing for perhaps two or three weeks of rest; the liquid sloshing and chugging of the deck swabbers; the occasional new creaks at times of heavy rolling, when half empty tanks of oil and of water released harmonious woody twangs and wheezes in the hull; the padded galloping of the two deck cats, who, from kittenhood, knew nothing of the world but the Zaca's deck. Nothing would ever lure them below; that was to them a dark inferno. They were alley cats, but with caste; they learned cat-fish from science-fish, and never forgot. (Plate 27.)

It was a wonderful life, this climbing a ladder to come home, to find the rigging hung with Vega, Canopus, Sirius, the North Star, the Southern Cross and odd planets, sometimes at the same moment. And the almanac became an old wives' tale when we considered our minimum of clothes at dinner on deck in mid-winter. Best of all, with and through it all, was the realization that we were going all out to try to add our mite to knowledge and to science. Templeton Crocker was a very wise man to spend even a small part of his life in this way.

CHAPTER XVIII

A DAY IN THE BAY OF PIEDRA BLANCA

THE western coast of Costa Rica is dappled with volcanoes. Some are cold and dead, their lava lifeless stone; others are molten and fiery at heart, sending up billowing clouds of smoke and gas—rhythmically or spasmodically. Still others have settled slowly downward, become filled with the waters of the Pacific, and changed their names from Craters to Bays.

On the first day of February the Zaca steamed into one of the most beautiful of these crater-formed bays, and in late afternoon, in perfect calm, our anchor chain ran out and came to rest on the bottom of the Bay of the White Stone— Piedra Blanca. I never recall a time when calmness of water was so appreciated by both ourselves and the crew.

A quick survey in the launch before dusk showed that we floated in the center of a very lovely, symmetrical horseshoe of encircling crater, a little hut at each end of the mile-wide crescent, dense jungle beyond a beach, part sand, part piled up rocks and cliffs; on the whole the perfect answer to a Naturalist's prayer. The water was sheer mirror and the gold and scarlet sunset might have been a terrific volcanic outburst far out at sea, throwing into black silhouette the great sentinel Piedra Blanca. Its beauty—but at this moment my trolling line was jerked almost out of my hand and a great sierra mackerel leaped high into the air. He was quite two feet long, full of fight, and by the time I had pulled him in and landed him my sunset had softened to violet and old rose. A new magic was wrought by the sliver of a crescent, with the full moon, oxydized but quite clear, within its horns.

The roe of the fish was brought to me when we returned to the yacht, and by careful estimate of fractional relative weight, I was rather shocked to realize that my brief, mid-sunset sport had cut short the potential lives of one million, six hundred and eighty thousand infant sierra mackerel! The mother mackerel appeared for the last time as a delicious filet at dinner.

Later as we sat peering through the darkness toward the unknown shore, the clear, high chirping of jungle crickets came across the water, and then, from a great distance, the ululations of the wildest, most sinister sound uttered by any animal in any continent—the coughing, resonant, grunting roars of a full-grown male howling monkey. If anyone can hear the chorus of these animals unmoved, he should confine his travels within the range of taxi-horns and the clangor of elevated trains.

Sunday, the sixth of February, was our last day in Piedra Blanca, and a typical Day of Rest, as we Zacásians interpreted it. Every day of the past week had been equally strenuous, but not so diversified. They had been filled rather with more routine collecting and exploring, the detailed account of which belongs to our scientific observations to be recorded elsewhere.

Early in the morning we three (Jocelyn Crane, John Tee-Van and myself) were towed to the sheltered inner part of the

216

bay. On the way a big swordfish leaped near us, and we passed a sleeping turtle and a pair of snowy egrets. We landed and worked the pools with excellent results, among the pailful retrieved being a golden yellow puffer and a hundred cardinal fish new to us. In one pool we found a crested blenny which had partly swallowed his distant cousin, a snake blenny, the posterior half of which was in turn being ingested by a sea urchin. After photographing this unbelievable triangle, we watched for five minutes. Seeing that the urchin was undoubtedly winning, I decided in favor of the fish.

Back in a small pool beneath overhanging jungle I secured two beautiful *Antennarius* or frogfish. So like were they in their mottled colours to the pink encrusting sponges and pool weed that we should never have found them, had one not swallowed a blenny so large and vigorously kicking that the frogfish was wrestled upside down by its still living meal. This reversal revealed underlying and conspicuous colours and blotches of brilliant orange and black, showing most prominently in the waters of the tidepool. Templeton discovered the first specimen of this undescribed species the day before.

In the shade of solid flower masses of Flor de Cortez and fragrant white frangipanni blossoms we waited for the tide to go down. A small native boy suddenly appeared, wading about apparently looking for edible shellfish. At last he discovered us, but when he caught our eye he turned away quickly and throughout a long walk over and around rocks he did not look again. The Zaca was probably the first vessel of any size ever to anchor in this bay; we were like a circus, movie, and radio, all in one, in his daily life. Yet he never looked again, the innate courtesy of the ancient Spaniard with the shyness of the modern Indian controlling him. After lunch I walked out and spoke to him. He greeted me with a shyness that hurt, and then suddenly rushed up to me, and seized my hand with a "*Buenos dias, qué tal, amigo,*" and looked up at me with the most charming smile I ever remember. His name proved to be Clemente Rosalez.

His shirt was little more than a "button and frill," but the pieces which had been sewed in, whole sections, had been matched so that the dark lines of the pattern were continuous. His battered straw hat was caught up at one side with a bit of coloured cord. The less said of his trousers the better; at best there was only one leg to them, perhaps a Costa Rican's concession to shorts. Clemente had fourteen years, had been to San José once and wondered if he could not go with me on the yacht to help catch fish and crabs, so I would have plenty to eat.

Later his father came and begged for quinine. He had lived at Santa Cruz until three years before and had had plenty of tortillas and other things which make life worth while, but his wife had been ill and the priests took all his money. There was no bitterness, just a statement of fact. His wife looked pure Indian and was good-humoured but stolid, while the little girl was as keen as her brother. Here in this isolated bay they lived apart from the world, with only a single family for neighbours in all directions.

I looked over to where Jocelyn was kneeling in the midst of the great intertidal sandy expanse, excavating at arm's length some unfortunate crab. When I looked again five minutes later, an infant pig, an equally juvenile dog and the Indian mother and sister of Clemente were all enthusiastically

218

at work on a quartet of holes, each probably inspired by some abstract, individual purpose. I could not recall ever having seen a more comic sight, until, soon afterwards, I watched them all set off for the lagoon together, and their travel was as funny as their digging; all in single file, in perfect alignment, Jocelyn, Rosalez *padre, madre, niña, perrito* and *puerco.*

Templeton brought from the Zaca a net-work, Christmas stocking half full of toys, which we gave to Clemente with injunctions to share them with his sister and with the horde of children watching us fearfully from the hut on the hill, and soon we heard them shrieking with emotion and blowing blasts on penny trumpets. Clemente begged the half-empty tins of sardines and the discarded crusts of bread which the hermit crabs had already begun to pre-empt. Speechless, all he could do was to swallow hard when I handed him half a dozen small fishhooks. Jocelyn gave the mother an empty quart jar with glass cover complete, which must have been beyond price in this shopless, mountain-bound bit of out-of-the-world. When we came to count up our own loot, we found that these few pools had yielded about eight hundred fish of at least twenty-seven species.

After having exhausted the pools of the inner bay, we landed on the huge, rock-bound cliffs of the outer eastern arm, fronting the open sea. Pe, our superhuman Samoan oarsman, jockeyed back and forth as near the water swirling against the rock surface as he dared. At the moment of highest swell, we each in turn leaped and clung, for all the world like the great crabs which scuttled about us, although we possessed only a fraction of their skill. Then our cameras, jars and other duffle were thrown up and caught, one by one. It was worth it, for we found strange life fronting the smashing breakers at low tide.

Along the outermost rim were small encampments of solid, weathered limpets, brownish or ivory-white against the black lava rocks. The limpets had been so battered and worn that the furrows were only visible at the base. They recalled the surface of the moon, or weathered and waterworn logs. Sometimes the summit was worn quite through to the transparent nacre of the inner lining, and I could see the inmate himself. The poetic thought came of the limpet looking out through his opaline window, watching the crashing waves at mid tide, and the great parrotfish at high, while at times of low tide he might see beautiful tropical butterflies as they passed. Unfortunately for this pleasant fantasy, limpets are quite blind, without even a light-sensitive spot at the apex of the body. A young soapfish in most unusual colouration defied me for a time, but by holding my breath during the spattering downpour of a wave which seemed to have gathered its impetus in Hawaii at least, I at last cornered and netted him, swallowing an enormous amount of the Pacific in the process.

Another great pool—or, rather inlet—was so lined and padded with a dense lining of seaweed that we trusted ourselves to its surge and flux, and secured excellent material by means of most exciting activities. The old football formula worked here as on any terrestrial gridiron: Stiffen and brace, and you were torn and scraped and hurt; let yourself roll and be swept along and you merely brushed harmlessly against the quilted ends and sides of this grand Brobdingnagian tub. Nine large puffers shared the pool with us, apparently amused at our awkwardness. Six of these were in the golden phase, and not only kept by themselves but were distinctly segregated into pairs. The remaining three were white-spotted regulars, except for one which had an irregular patch of orange on one side of the body.

After signaling for the launch, I walked on along the outer line of cliffs, along the open, southern shore line of Costa Rica. The intermingling of granite and lava resulted in beautiful columns, delicate tints and fantastic sculpturing. Large, clear pools reflecting the sunshine and blue sky, waited for the next of the seven hundred and thirty refreshing baths of the year's tides. Rounding a curve and squeezing through a narrow cleft forbidden to any except my particular type of build, I came upon a strangely perfect flight of steps, twelve or fifteen, with hints even of a lava balustrade. At the bottom I turned a second corner and saw Aladdin's cave—a great hemispherical cavern of utmost beauty, overhung with flowering vines, a central pool filled with brilliant fish, and a long-tailed bronze hummingbird searching the walls for whatever a hummingbird might expect to find in a cavern of the sea. I walked on to explore it, but was abruptly stopped by a great gash clear across the terrace from sea to cliff, fifteen feet of sheer gorge. I began to let myself down into the emerald inlet to swim across to the cave, when a six-foot wall of water swept in, and crashed below me with cruel force. The Cave of Aladdin was well guarded. I remembered what Slith and Slorg did when they came to the Crack in the World. I too turned back. It was a satisfying climax to a day of exploration. (Plate 26.)

In late afternoon we took a last walk along the west jungle trail, past the giant trees looped and draped with lianas and cereus. In places the ground was covered with a solid carpet of wild poincianas, frangipannis and tassel flowers. Tracks of tapir, deer and raccoons and small cats dotted the muddied places, and we jumped a peccary. Three lovely squirrels, grizzled gray above and rich rufous below, were making a terrible racket over a small, green, tree snake just out of our reach. One of the squirrels was anxious to cross the trail at the exact spot where I stood. It objected strenuously to my existence, and cursed me roundly. Its usual note sounded exactly like the drumming of a woodpecker. When excited, this increased in volume and rapidity, the entire body of the little animal so throbbing with the recoil of the vocal explosions that I expected to see it shake itself loose from the branch. Finally the outburst merged into the liquid chatter of our gray squirrel. Another persistent sound was the calling of large jungle doves, loud and ventriloquial, *Wheeeeeeeeeeo, cock-cock-a-too, cock-cock-a-too*. It was a nice jungle with only a single mosquito at a time, and no bête rouge or ticks.

I stopped for a few minutes under the flowering balsa tree, where a few days before I recorded twenty-six species of birds in about a half hour. Among these were antwrens, antshrikes, woodhewers, manakins, tanagers, flycatchers and puffbirds. I also recognized eight species of hummingbirds and missed many more. No one can ever be accused of overstatement in any common name he chooses to apply to these marvelous creatures, such as fork-tailed wood nymph, white-breasted fairy, pygmy coquette and curve-billed emerald. In beauty and in bizarre feathering they defy all human labels.

A shift of wind and tide had raised six lines of enthusiastic breakers, but we fought our way through them with no instru-

222

24. Marooned with a Seven-foot Boa Constrictor on the Shore of Port Parker, Costa Rica.

ment wetted. Small sharks were about us as we clambered on board waist-deep, but harmless as we have always found them. As we reached the smooth swells, a flyingfish shot out just ahead, and swiftly after it a big sierra mackerel, shooting up and up in a straight line, completely missing its intended victim but rising to a height of at least twenty feet. We all saw it, or it would scarcely be credited. When it turned at the zenith of the leap, it came down in an equally straight line.

On our way back to the Zaca we pulled a last shallow dredge, and got two lancelets—those primitive near-fish—together with a few rare crabs, butterflyfish, flounders and stargazers. It is fortunate that with our varied equipment we are able to tap so many fields of marine life. With our skins bruised and muscles aching from battling the solid waters of the outer shore, it was a relief simply to sit in the launch, let the dredge drag over the bottom, pull it up, and empty its treasures into a convenient tray.

At nine o'clock at night, seven miles out from shore, when again the slender moon had followed the sun into the Pacific, we stopped the engines for our regular night light work. Before we had lost way, the darkness was filled with the soft sighing of a multitude of dolphins. All around us they silently rose, sent out a sibilant, spray-filled sigh and noiselessly sank again.

Small flyingfish, shrimps, millions of copepods and oikpleura came at once, and were followed by regiments of squids, small and large, which kept the illumined water murky with their barrage of ink clouds. When we were again under way, and our eyes had forgotten the glare of the light, the tropical stars came down until they seemed just to clear the tips of the masts, all in perfect order as mankind has always

223

25. *Laboratory on the Zaca*, unlimbered for work in the quiet waters of some bay.

found them, the North Star low down, the Southern Cross recumbent and well up. The oblique, cosmic circle of circles was blazing, with Aries, Taurus, Gemini, Leo in full view, and most appropriately for us, Cancer and Pisces.

When the last specimen had been labeled and corked, the last note written, at the very end of this fullest of full days, I went down to my cabin, gloriously tired, with a mind so filled with a jumble of scientific problems and puzzles that I reached up to my book rack and read myself to sleep with "Piers Plowman:" "I was weary of wandringe and went me to reste."

CHAPTER XIX

NIGHT CALLS AT SEA
(with Eric Liljencrantz)

AND so we bade good-by forever to the Bay of the White Rock. However, little did we know . . . etc., etc.

Two days later, we were well out at sea off the Gulf of Nicoya. I was perched on the poop of the Zaca watching the angle of the slender wire which led obliquely down into the ultramarine water. When struck, it vibrated and sang like a taut piano wire, and no wonder, for its full mile of quarter-inch thickness was bearing the terrific strain of a series of great nets dragged through the black, icy depths.

All unknown to our scientific group, through the soundless invisible air overhead, there came ripples or whirlpools (who shall find a real simile?) of long and short, infinitesimal, stuttering waves, and through the ears and brain and hands of our radio operator, they were resolved at last into visible words and phrases. "Help, help!" was the gist of the message; "a very sick man on the tunaboat San Salvador needs a doctor. His symptoms are dot, dash, dot. Please help."

Such a spate of volumes about varied activities of physicians and surgeons has been poured forth in recent years that it is almost like a revival of the Lucy and Rollo Books: Doctors at Work, Physicians at Play; Surgeons in War; Physicians' Philosophy, Doctors' Ideas, Surgeons as Human Beings, etc.

225

There is one dramatic phase, however, in the lives of these wonderful men which I have not seen mentioned.

In war men do all in their power to maim and kill one another, yet when wounded enemies are captured, instead of being subjected to a logical process of extermination they are taken to hospitals, cured if possible, exchanged for other cured prisoners and shot at all over again. I suppose it is the remains of the almost extinct idea of chivalry. Probably there are aviators who would hesitate at driving a sword through a woman or a baby who, without demur, will drop bombs on them when disguised as "civilian population." We read and hear of sudden cases of critical illness in our neighbourhood, and doctors are at once sent for. Yet ultimate cure or death does not hold our interest for a moment provided we do not know the afflicted or his immediate relations.

But when, in all directions, through blazing sunshine or black, stormy night there goes across the water a series of silent, quivering radio waves, "Man desperately ill; symptoms are dot, dash, dot, what shall we do?" every hospital and every doctor within reach springs to attention, and a score of captains estimate their distance and course. Succour, first in the shape of advice and as soon as possible in the form of an onrushing steamer, is the result. And, too, this particular man becomes a center of interest to hundreds of seamen and ocean travelers. His isolation on the ocean stimulates the imagination and stirs the sympathy as would never be the case with a human being so afflicted on land.

To return to our own radio call: after a complex exchange of messages we found that we were the nearest ship, three hundred and fifty miles away, although a physician on a big liner on the Atlantic side had sent suggestions over sea and jungle. Templeton promised the aid of our capable doctor, Eric Liljencrantz, and the winch began to turn and the mile of wire to come in. It was beyond the power of our machinery to reel fast, so after an hour, the nets arrived at the surface as usual, revealing, one by one, their strange contents: slender, black eels caught in the mesh by their incredibly long, curved jaws, squids splayed out with their suckers still clinging tightly to whatever they touched and their great eyes staring wide at the unknown sunlight. Finally, the glass jars were untied, each filled with an unearthly medley of creatures, many with brilliant lights still glowing as they had in the eternal darkness of their haunts a half mile down. All represented for us the acme of scientific interest.

The propeller began turning as the terminal lead weight bumped on board, and we headed northward again, full speed. The tunaboat was in such-and-such latitude, wallowing toward us in a bad Papagayan sea, and an intermediate meeting place was settled upon.

And so it came about, at sunset, three days after we had said farewell, we again anchored in Piedra Blanca. Through the gathering dusk I could make out the familiar white sentinel, the tiny huts, and I knew exactly where were Aladdin's Cave and the balsa trees with their teeming bird life.

I listened, but heard no noise of howling monkeys, and even the crickets were silent. Strangest of all, a half hour of submarine light showed not a single fish or squid. I had a weird feeling that all life had ceased with our going. Then a cluster of tiny figures, our friends, appeared on the beach, and faintly there came through the gloom, calls dimmed by dis-

tance into a faint *Uluoo!* and then silence. We settled down
for a quiet night in a world as noiseless as the sunset, with no
sound of wind or surf.

But another silent message came, sooner than we expected,
and stirred us into instant life: the tunaboat would meet us
far off shore, coming south through the storm, full speed.
The crew was called, the anchor came up, running lights were
set, and we swung around and out for a second last time,
northward into the abominable Papagayo. At four in the
morning amidst tempestuous waves, we sighted the lights of
the *San Salvador*. As to what followed, I have asked Dr. Liljencrantz to let me use the notes of his journal.

"She's off the bow now, doctor. We'll be ready in about
fifteen minutes. Here's some coffee."

Thus had the surgeon been roused at four o'clock, as the
Zaca sloshed along a northwesterly course off the Costa Rican
coast. The scene that greeted him as he stumbled sleepily on
deck was one of compelling beauty, long to be vividly remembered. Bright starlight and a cloudless sky, yet the *Zaca* was
tossing on a troubled sea in the warm tropic wind. During the
night it had reached gale proportions but was now subsiding.
The surface had been stirred into choppy swells, each with
its phosphorescent crest, a strange setting of unrest.

Off the bow, a ship's lights were apparent, running lights
augmented by brighter beams. As the ships approached, flashlights spoke in code:

"Zaca?"

"Yes, *San Salvador*."

The two ships approached each other cautiously. The outlines of the tunaboat could now be made out.

228

Again the flashlights spoke:

"Have you a boat ready?"

"Yes, we are lowering away."

The Zaca hove to.

The throaty voice of *San Salvador's* diesel could be heard intermittently as she maneuvered to provide a lee for her boat. A long wait and additional conversation in code.

Finally a boat appeared, proceeding unsteadily toward the completion of a high-seas rendezvous which had been arranged forty hours before. The reports had heralded critical illness. Appendicitis? Adhesions? Obstruction? Ulcer? None of these would be rendered a less difficult problem by the day-and-a-half delay, or by having only the cabin of a fishing boat to serve as a hospital.

The rowboat drew alongside, manned by four sturdy oarsmen and a coxswain. But for the lack of pistols and cutlasses, it might have been the boarding crew out of any pirate tale. The first vocal hail was thick with Portuguese accent, and my mind went back to old accounts of the ancestors of these men. They were grand old navigators who discovered and annexed Brazil, equatorial Africa, Madagascar, and portions of India, China and the Malay Peninsula; they searched out a waterway to India, and it was a Portuguese sailor who first circumnavigated the globe.

The transfer of medical gear was accomplished under hazard. Handled as a football, a heavy case containing a precious microscope almost followed a flashlight into the angry spray. But the shift was completed through luminescent swells without further incident; and the *San Salvador* was boarded with gear and personnel intact.

229

The patient's state of distress was acute. No less acute was the surgeon's state of apprehension, after the prolonged anticipation of an immediate surgical emergency. Fate, however, was kind. The clinical picture turned out to be clearly that of renal colic rather than intestinal obstruction. It was a comparatively simple matter to ease his pain, and to preside over the delivery of a large kidney stone.

The relief of all concerned was considerable, and the relaxed tension, as the medical exigency abated, allowed all hands to contemplate breakfast with enthusiasm. It then transpired that the patient was the cook; and much robust humour arose from the selection of three volunteers to substitute for him. Whatever they may have lacked in experience was more than offset by enthusiasm, and the result of their efforts lacked neither quality nor quantity. A choice of fruits was offered; cereals, omelette, bacon, potatoes, toast, milk and coffee followed. Bronzed Mediterranean faces, punctuated by occasional gold incisors, grinned in appreciation. The surgeon sat in astonishment at how even sea air and hard labour could stimulate such monumental appetites. Adequate explanation of the true reason soon followed.

The sea had quieted considerably, and from the lookout at the masthead, announcement was made in a foghorn voice, of a school of tuna off the port bow. Immediately, all hands swung into action, with the easy precision of a varsity team, to provide a dynamic spectacle unsurpassed by any staged on an athletic field.

As the course was altered to overtake the school, two chummers began to throw out live bait from the great tanks on the elevated poop. Over the port gunwales, iron gratings were lowered to water level. On these gratings, constantly awash, ten massive men took their stand, shoulder to shoulder, armed with bamboo rods. To these rods were attached, by short lines, lures of brass and feathers, together with vicious-looking barbless hooks. Strikes began immediately, and with deft movements, ten-pound tuna were hurled in quick succession back over the line of rodsmen to the deck.

The live-bait anchovies, descending in a barely discernable arc, seemed to rush back out of the water transformed into massive live projectiles. Not an instant passed without struggling fish fighting in full flight, and at times five and six could be counted in the air at once. The deck soon became a seething, shimmering mass. The crescendo bedlam of slapping tails on the deck, grunting men and splashing water filled the air. From the masthead the surgeon watched a never-ending surge of purple forms rushing by, below the turquoise surface. A sizable squadron of frigatebirds soon collected to claim any stray bait overlooked by this horde.

The spectacle lasted for a full half hour, then abruptly subsided. Six tons of stranded, still struggling fish completely covered the decks. A new and frosty home was awaiting them. There followed careful washing and stowing of the catch in the ice-cold refrigerated hold.

Meanwhile the patient rested comfortably, and was convinced with difficulty that he need not fear further bouts of agony. The surgeon returned to the Zaca. The radioed report next day was that the patient was symptom free, and eager to return to work.

We examined the food of several tuna which the doctor brought back with him, and found it similar to that of tunas

in the West Indies. Besides a few just swallowed live bait
thrown out by the fishermen, the bulk of the food was hundreds upon hundreds of the larvae of squilla. It becomes a
constantly increasing mystery why these great, husky, strong-
swimming fish, with all the small fish of the open sea from
which to chose, should select these perfectly transparent,
glassy crustaceans less than an inch in length, flat as a sheet
of paper, composed of hard crust and spines with only sufficient organic substance to hold all these together and flip
them through the water. A less nourishing diet would be
impossible to imagine.

Until now the occupations of our physician were attending
to the minor ills of ourselves and the crew and enthusiastically
helping in our scientific work. But his fame soon spread, and
hardly had we tied up to the wharf at Puntarenas in the Gulf
of Nicoya than a message came that the *Belle of Portugal* had
a dying man on board. And the doctor reported that this
seemed no exaggeration. Sitting in the galley, naked except
for the oil-soaked cotton with which he had been covered,
was Bob Hargrove, offering a stoical grin of greeting. Severe
burns are a nightmare of medical practice, their victims are
unsung heroes. An explosion in the gasoline launch had struck
this chap full force, resulting in deep burns over half of his
body surface. To make the tale short, our physician flew with
him up over the mountains to the splendid hospital at the
capital, San José, where all possible was done for him. A
miracle was wrought, and fifty hours later he was definitely
pronounced out of danger, a result due as much to his own
superb courage as to skillful treatment.

Anchored in the Gulf was a fleet of these tunaboats, the

Flying Cloud, Westgate, Senator, Sea Boy, Jenny Rose, San Rafael, Santa Teresa, Victoria, Forest, Chicken of the Sea and *Sea Tern.* We were to become better acquainted with more than one of them in days to come, for these fishermen live hard lives, and even their tough frames reached the limits of endurance.

A transfusion of blood in the open, uneasy sea was given to a seaman on board the *Forest.* The captain and every one of his mates offered their blood, but in spite of everything the man died quietly at dawn from an illness of long standing. As Dr. Liljencrantz said, under such circumstances the origin of the name *Zaca* was brought to mind—among California Indians, it is the word for Peace.

CHAPTER XX

SAN JOSE AND THE ISLE OF JASPER

AFTER several days, anchored near the wharf at Puntarenas and exploring the surrounding mangroves and islands, we went to San José, the capital of Costa Rica. At five o'clock on the morning of the fourteenth of February we had a quick breakfast, and left in the launch with little time to spare to catch the train, but with an absurdly enormous full moon, deep orange, caught in the act of setting. A customs soldier hailed us, but we said "Hello," and went on. With trailing gun and bayonet he trotted by our side, sending forth a perfect spate of indistinguishable Spanish, while I answered with the multiplication table in equally fluent English. His excitement increased with our speed, and we were soon all in high gear pounding along the water front, reaching our train just as it began blowing off steam, and as the conductor decided to wait another hour before starting. A feeble wave and grin from our armed escort, as we eventually pulled out, showed there was no hard feeling, and we turned the rear platform into an observation stance.

For the first hour the lights and shadows made of everything a different world, somewhat as they do before sunset. At these times there are two things at work to make us stop whatever we are doing and pay attention to the earth and to ourselves. First, is a sense of the rapidity of time. When once the sun establishes itself well up in the sky, the day becomes static. In the course of hours we are reminded by twinges of hunger or by bodily weariness that mid-day is at hand, but the glare and the comparative lack of shadows and perspective absorbs our sight and reflects no disturbing stimulus. But at dusk and dawn the clock of time ticks loudly. Especially in this early morning hour, refreshed and with these amazing long shadows, and unusual underlighting of things which later will be darkened, we must pay attention. And here we had the added excitement of a new and strange country, so we were fairly drunk with concentration.

The early morning flight of fork-tailed flycatchers was the first dominant thing. They must roost in one place in enormous numbers, and at daybreak scatter, as at Corinto, all over the country. At first I saw them in fifties, then fewer, a dozen at a time as they easily kept up with the crawling train. Then birds in pairs, and finally a solitary bird which alighted on a telegraph wire, and, before we passed out of sight, had begun flycatching.

Nothing could have been better than this train, winding along switchbacks, then backing again, stopping at every little village which had the smallest bit of freight to be taken on or put off. Now and then we passed over slender, cobwebby bridges, across deep barrancas with a thread of white water at the bottom. Usually, however, the train took its time and wandered around the rim, making hairpins, horseshoes, almost figures of eight. The electric engine was clean and quiet and quite patient with our desire to go slowly. Soon we began climbing towards the clouds, and a gray shadow would drift down, close about us, and cover the surrounding mountains with cottony profiles—through half-closed eyes seeming the Himalayan snows again.

Tortillas, cashews and star-apples were held up for purchase when we stopped, and after a time I discovered what appeared strange about the men: hardly one seen on the whole trip carried a revolver. In this and a hundred other ways Costa Rica stood far above the other republics we had visited.

Most of the fences in this country are alive. The acacias and other woods are cut into posts and connected by several strands of barbed wire. At once the posts begin to grow lustily and to "swallow" the wire. The acacias make a bit of a fuss at this, and send out a blackened, protecting protuberance, as if the foreign body actually irritated the tissues. Into the other kinds of wood the wire slips as if through thick molasses, with no evidence of contour or bark. In time the boles increase in diameter until they begin to close up the intervals between post and post, the wire rusting and falling away, leaving the fields bounded by a straight line of trees almost touching one another. Toward the end of the trip gusts of air rushed up the gorges, almost blowing us off the platform, the wind grew cooler and the mountains came rapidly nearer and lower, their sides covered with long-leaved pines and eucalyptus.

At San José we were met by my old friend and most excellent scientist, Dr. Anastasio Alfaro, until recently director of the national museum. It was a delight to find the latter well appointed and with interesting collections. All the fishes and crabs had been put out on tables for our study, and we spent much time in these rooms. The kindly and capable director, Dr. Valerio Rodriguez, did everything in his power to aid our work and was justly proud of the museum in his charge.

From my hotel window I could see the volcano of Irazu rising in its majesty above the city, and the cool days and cool nights revealed the high altitude of this up-to-date city. In comfort and general beauty it has no rival between San Diego and Panama.

The poisonous-snake department at the great hospital was of particular interest and was shown to us by the kindness of Dr. Beeche. A complete collection of species was preserved, including what appear to be record sizes for both fer-de-lance and bushmaster, each almost exactly seven feet one inch. The venom was taken every two weeks from live snakes and in the crystallized form sent to the famous serum institution at São Paulo, Brazil. Ampules of the serum were returned, and these distributed throughout Costa Rica. They were given free in exchange for more live snakes, so the supply was continuous. The average number of bites was sixty a month, although of course there were many which were not reported. This was in excess of the number in Panama, but the explanation was that there was a much greater amount of cultivation. This resulted in an immense increase of rats and mice, and consequently of venomous snakes.

The serum was effective for fer-de-lance and rattlesnake poison but not for bushmaster, although it was said to lessen the virulence of the latter's bite. Fortunately, bushmasters were not common. Very few bites were reported from coral snakes, due apparently to the small mouth and short fangs. Only one sea snake had been taken in the Gulf of Nicoya, and this was kept in health for five months by constant changes of salt water.

On my arrival I was introduced to an entomologist by the name of Ferdinand Nevermann, scientifically a free lance, but whose position was manager of a large banana finca on the Port Limón or Atlantic side of the country. We became great friends, and I found that his interest in insects and other creatures was as trenchant and keen as that of a man like William Morton Wheeler. I spent much time at his house going over his collections, and found a world of new things. He had about fifty thousand Costa Rican beetles, most of them named, but best of all was his knowledge of their habits and the reasons for their strange adaptations of structure. His elephant beetles, males, females and development stages, were most interesting. The grubs were in some cases full six inches long and an inch through. He told of the amusing native beliefs concerning these giants, how the males waged terrible battles with their horns, the victor finally carrying off the female, held crosswise in his jaws! He told as a fact, however, that it is difficult to get perfect specimens, for the jaws are in great demand by the peons. They are ground up and dropped into the drink of a girl by her lovesick swain, in a sincere belief in their effectiveness. For this purpose they sell for ten colones, or about one dollar and forty cents.

The most interesting things in his collections were the army ants and other ant guests and parasites. The beetles and bugs and even wasps which marched with the soldiers, or rode on their legs or backs or under their bodies, were in great numbers, and in extremes of adaptations beyond any that I had seen or collected in British Guiana. Small and large they

238

26. *Bay of Piedra Blanca.* Looking across the impassable gulf into Aladdin's Cave.

were, some looking exactly like ants, some swollen, or burnished and varnished against attack; others three times as long as the ants, yet with such shadow markings that in rapid motion they must undoubtedly have resembled their hosts; beetles with sweet glands and without; others so like trigonid bees that for months Nevermann threw them away, thinking them slightly imperfect hymenopteran individuals; brenthids with sexes so varying in size that he had seen an inch and a quarter male trying to mate with a female one quarter inch in length and vice versa.

The termite guests, more familiar to me, were mostly rove beetles, with camouflaged, upturned abdomens; and Ptilidae, which include the smallest beetles in the world, minute, brown specks of life one hundredth of an inch in length, living chiefly in soft, spongy, tree fungi. He showed me what appeared to be undeveloped larvae, which had suddenly begun to lay eggs, which he was trying to raise, and so on unendingly. Each day I would return to my fish with new insights and beliefs in unsuspected possibilities of evolution.

The kindness and trouble which this man showed and took to satisfy my deep interest were beyond words. When we left he boarded the train and rode as far as the first station. In a curio shop I had seen a box of rare but indifferently mounted beetles for sale, and at the last minute I gave Nevermann the money and he promised to get them and send them to the Zaca. Two days later there arrived a box filled to overflowing with several hundred of the pick of the things I was interested in, ant guests, parasites, mimics, a wealth of the marvels of evolution as shown in Costa Rican insects. We had arranged for correspondence from which we both hoped to sustain and

239

27. "Nameless." The Zaca's cat in her favourite hide-out. In all her life this cat had never been below decks or ashore.

develop the enthusiasm with which we seemed to inspire each other. (Plate 29.)

When I reached New York, in place of a letter from Nevermann, a note from his daughter told of his going out at night into the jungle near his banana plantation and, while collecting beetles in the stump of a tree, being mistaken for a deer by an American sportsman, and shot dead.

The great Gulf of Nicoya was too huge to be of interest in the same way as our preceding twenty-odd bays. But scattered about it were bevies of islands and islets, and around these we dived and dredged and explored pools and woods. Jasper Island stood out in beauty and interest. As our launch nosed gently against the pebbles on the lee side, my old butterfly friend *Junonia coenia* fluttered down and alighted on the bow and I felt that Jasper Island welcomed me. A great tree which had watched centuries come and go shaded the beach, and a straggling path up a bank led to the only house on the island. It was in use but deserted, and the walls of woven sticks and thatch were thoroughly air-conditioned. Every utensil lay about, apparently unwashed after many meals, and there was a dilapidated bunk and a heap of threadbare clothes. No Dyak or Zulu would have acknowledged it. But a waterworn board, supported by three sticks, bore a dented tin can with the dregs of a burned-out candle, and behind this a coloured sheet from a Bayer's Quinine Almanac with a print of the Virgin —the focus of the tin, candle, shelf—and the pitiful little shrine took on a dignity, and the hut seemed somehow different.

After five minutes on the trodden earth I found at least half a hundred excited fleas hopefully hopping up my sneakers and socks, and I hurried outside. In the compound, several bunches of ancient bananas were hanging from near-by stakes. They had long since passed beyond the ordinary rotting stage, and gave forth a wholly strange and powerful odour. As so often in the tropics, this unpleasant aura attracted a cloud of beautiful butterflies and other insects: great longicorn beetles, bird-sized morphos, bluer than any sky, skippers waving their tails excitedly, and flies of fire opal, performing intricate dipteran dances on the rim of the irresistible fruit.

We walked slowly across the small island, coming out on a delightful cove with a sandy beach, a cluster of coconut palms, and a single, enormous fig tree. The ways of plants can be as exciting as those of animals. The limbs of this banyan-like fig stretched out and out from the main trunk, sloping gently, beginning forty feet up and ending within a yard of the sand. Normal branches sprouted from the sides of the larger limbs as in all well-behaved trees, until one suddenly appeared directly *beneath*. It was gray and lichen-mottled like the rest, but after descending several feet it did something no normal fig branch ever did—it divided into two or more terminal shoots. These continued to descend and became soft and malleable. From now on, all similarity with the upper part of the tree was lost. These naked, sunlit roots high in mid-air rebranched, forked, bifurcated, and, as they descended, braided themselves together, clutching and twisting and intertwining until they formed a tightly woven cable an inch across, with more tendrils dripping from the end, reaching and straining for the earth below. If the branches of a leafless poplar, like the tall, slender ones along French roads, should suddenly close up and braid themselves together, and then the whole tree turn upside down and take root high up on some other tree, we would have a reasonably accurate resemblance to one of these scores of air roots of the fig of Jasper Island. There was never a recalcitrant or treasonable twig or tendril; never did one of these earth-conscious sprouts ever attempt to reach up and away from its nadir-pledged skein of fellows. Leaves and flowers were utterly inconceivable, wholly alien to its destiny. The position of the ventral sprout, high overhead, had decided this forever. I cut through one of these aerial cables and found eighty-two component strands, fibers or other elements. I was surrounded by hundreds of these swaying lattices and portieres of threads, cords and cables, forming a living nexus of beauty.

On the farther side of the fig, high up among the branches, some bird long ago dropped a seed in a knothole or a crevice of bark, a seed which had sprouted and grown. This heavenly graft was of a plume blossom tree, and over a good portion of trunk and eastern branches of the fig, myriads of lovely pink and white flowers pretended that the great tree was all their own.

Fifty yards away was a scraggly dead tree, its bare branches making the most of a transient crop of flaming fruit—fifteen great red and blue macaws. Their guttural but liquid craaawks came to me, softened by distance, and I watched them for a long time, as they perched in pairs close together, forever preening one another. When they turned on their perch their long tails often caught and twisted against the twigs. The odd bird perched alone and had to be content with arranging his own plumage.

As I watched the macaws through my binoculars I saw an

astonishing sight which must have one of only three possible explanations: either a macaw has a keen appreciation of a practical joke, or the lack of sense of the proverbial Irishman and his saw out on a limb, or else a tropical beetle grub had burrowed into and weakened a certain dead branch. I saw one of a pair of the birds deliberately bite hard at the branch on which he and his mate were perched, and instantly, at that very point, the branch broke and the birds fell several feet in a confused jumble of brilliant plumage and of squawks which reached to high heaven. They upset a second pair beneath, and the entire assembly went wild with emotion, waving widespread wings and shattering the island's silence beyond repair. Complete calm was never restored and after an interval all flew off, two and two, an unbroken stream of vocal "Didyoueverinyourlifes" and "Wellwaddyeknowaboutthats" coming back to me. The lone bird talked aloud to himself as long as he was within hearing.

An inch-long digger wasp in armour of black and gold was frantically excavating at my very feet. Pit after pit she dug, then hovered in the air a few seconds for an airplane view, only to descend and start a fresh one. For half an hour, life for her was only a search for a better 'ole. Then she left, and a few minutes later I saw that she was carrying some prey of good size beneath her body. This had no effect upon her digging and she made the sand fly as usual, four strokes to the second. The front legs must be folded together or arranged in some way so that they form a scoop or shovel, so efficiently do they operate. This last hole seemed satisfactory, and swiftly the sloping tunnel grew. When the pile of debris became too large, she backed slowly up the flume, flicking as

243

she went. Her farthest flung grains fell over the rim of the pit of an antlion, which instantly hurled them back with interest, under the delusion that the sand slide was caused by the sideslipping of some approaching prey. This world of sand was inhabited by a special cosmos of diminutive life, as complex as it was exciting.

The wasp at last had struck the pay dirt to which she could entrust her prey and the egg she would attach to it. How like the Indians of old on this very peninsula, who buried food, grain, grinding stone and gold ornaments for use in a future life. How like but how infinitely more practical was this great wasp.

Close to Jasper Island was a steep, rocky islet, not more than three hundred yards in diameter, thickly beset with stubby trees on the upper slopes. To this all the frigatebirds of Nicoya and a goodly proportion of the pelicans and boobies came each night and slept. At seven in the morning more than one thousand of the former were more or less asleep, two-thirds being white-headed birds of the year, and most of the remainder full-grown males. On the rocks at the base were quantities of boobies, all enmity with the pirate frigates forgotten in night and sleep. An hour later, however, most of the boobies left, heading swiftly out to sea, evidently to make certain of an undisturbed breakfast, no matter what might happen to later meals when their bed-fellow brigands appeared.

The pelicans kept somewhat to themselves, and this may well have been forced by differences in the method of waking. The frigatebirds lifted their heads, looked around, sat scrunched up for a few minutes, then quietly dropped from their perch. A pelican would poke his head and beak out from beneath his plumage blanket, look about, stretch one wing after the other, then elongate his neck and beak skyward, and yawn as only a pelican or a hippopotamus can. This routine was often interfered with by irate neighbours, whose slumber and balance were rudely interrupted by these early pelicaniform jerks. I saw more than one bird knocked off his perch, or the branch itself broken in these matutinal rows.

Little by little, in loose companies of ten or more, the frigates left, many of them to scoop up a few beakfuls of water and return for another snooze. At one-thirty in early afternoon every bird had gone, but at three o'clock the first contingent for the night arrived, and at sunset every tree and rock was solidly filled, with frigates, boobies and pelicans again. Two nights in succession I identified individual frigates and pelicans by missing primaries, and saw them alight on the same part of the branch of identical trees as the night before.

Early in the morning after the day on Jasper I was awakened by silence. After rooster calls, automobile horns, shouts of *"Diarrrrrrrrrrrrrrio!"* from the lusty throats of newsboys in San José, the something which for me, these days, was set at six-thirty, clicked, and I was instantly wide awake, listening to the silence: the padded galloping over my head of Nameless and No-one, the two deck cats, the swabbing squad, these, together with the pleasantly unsynchronized belling of the half hours by the ship's clocks, these were all. Then my eye caught sight of something on my doorknob, and the shock to my eye was like a shriek to the ear. On Christmas night Templeton had played Santa Claus and thumbtacked a huge, filled stocking to the wall of each of our cabins without

245

waking us. I thought rapidly. This was the twenty-second of February. What was that? Oh, yes, Washington's Birthday. But one did not give or receive gifts on this occasion, even a stuffed bird, a badly stuffed owl.

I sat up, and my stuffed bird turned two great yellow eyes upon me, and softly flew out of the door. I followed, and looked up the companionway and saw four eyes gazing full face down at me, Nameless and No-one staring into the black depths below decks, where they had never dared venture. Hardly had I focused on these when a shadow drifted over my head, silhouetted for a moment against the lighter awning and vanished, together with the heads of the cats. A Costa Rican screech owl had paid me a fleeting visit, having flown from, and apparently back to the nearest land, Jasper Island.

CHAPTER XXI

GOLFITO: BAY OF JUNGLES

WHEN we left Nicoya and put out to sea we entered upon the last phase of our southward trek, the humid tropical zone, with its supreme achievement in earthly plant and animal life —the tropical rain forest. Twenty-three miles off shore we put out the night light and waited for our usual nocturnal miracle. On this first evening in March the miracle materialized, but not in the way we expected. On the whole it was a poor evening for fish, but an abundance of plankton fog, mostly the small compressed shrimplets known as amphipods. A few coppery squirrelfish and anchovies appeared and vanished, or were caught. Baby flyingfish hurried about, not wanting to come near, but unable to resist. Squids now and then submarined into the radius of light, snatched a fish and backed off into the darkness again.

I gave over my watch to someone and went below. At eleven-thirty an uproar on deck might have been a whale at the light or a man overboard. A moment later Templeton came down the companion stairs in tremendous excitement and dragged me willingly up to see the smallest baby Pacific sailfish ever captured. I awakened George Swanson, my artist, to record the bright colours before they faded. This sailfish was only one and three-quarters inches long as compared with the three and a quarter youngster which we had taken six weeks before and twelve hundred miles farther north. (Plate 14.)

We strained our eyes at the light but no other was seen, although the appearance and capture of a half-inch fish nearly caused heart attacks until we identified it as an infant dolfin. When I came to study the littlest of little sailfish I found only minor differences from the slightly larger one. Not until we can find one less than an inch can we really get a detailed idea of the early development of the elongate beak and ventral fins and the mighty sail, which even in this tiny creature are absurdly like those of a nine-foot sailfish.

At the night light of the next evening we were concentratedly sailfish-conscious, to use a horrid modernism, but for two full minutes after the light shone out, sending its greenish glow in all directions, not a fish of any kind came into sight. Only the usual faint mist of minute life drifting irrevocably, drawn as by a magnet to the glare. Then, with a sudden rush, the water was filled with an innumerable host of silvery anchovies, with an outer penumbra of thread herrings. These circled so swiftly that, as I looked down with half-closed eyes, the fish appeared fused, and there below me was a whirring wheel of pale silver in the greenish water. It was a slightly eccentric wheel, for the multitude was so great that they compressed into a narrower, deeper mass near the side of the Zaca, spreading out as they banked sharply around the outer three-quarters of the circle. Occasionally single, silvery shuttles of large jacks shot through the concentric rings of life, bringing death to some fish at each dash. Now and then one would bore straight through and through the wheel, even against the animated current, strangely causing no commotion, though it snatched an anchovy as it went. But when several plunged, in a spearhead, at once and close together, the whole wheel was warped with fear, and frayed out into a hundred terrified separate fish. A moment later, the spell of the light induced forgetfulness, snapped them back and they sank into individual obliteration. From a few yards up the ratlines the scene was like an elliptical galaxy, an aquatic spiral nebula. Then another simile would rush to mind, and like a thread of gold woven through cloth of silver a great runula would dash through, or on the outer rim a mirror-round moonfish would heliograph its presence with full side view, seize a sardine and go into eclipse, all at the same instant.

Uvita Bay was a place of touch and go with us, using the phrase only in the sense of time and space, yet it left an indelible impression, an impression of unexpected and pleasant surprises. The distance, as a booby flies, from our last bay, Nicoya, was only seventy miles, but in vegetation, bird and insect life and general feel of the whole, it might easily have been a thousand. For it was real tropics, a potent introduction to all our succeeding ports of call. Also physical geography and the curve of the earth were abruptly made real when we reset our watches, before going ashore, to New York time—so far and so unconsciously had we been swinging eastward as well as south from our start on the island of sea-elephants.

My brief vignette of Uvita will be only a series of staccato sentences. Enormous ranges of mountains shut off all the drought of more northern coasts, and initiated the wonderful open-air greenhouse of the tropics, born of sun and rain. The name Uvita Bay is synonymous with a tiny dent in the shore line, where the rollers held sway, and we landed at our risk. This isolation made the natives happy, friendly, trusting, contented, independent and altogether nice folk. They raised enormous bunches of bananas which, as there were no vessels or railroad, they dried and shipped as flour on burro back, or in oxcarts with gorgeously painted wheels of solid wood. If the bananas spoiled before drying, they became the food of pigs and butterflies, and happiness was enjoyed by all in this delightful, unreal land. People delayed their meals, they let their burros stand, they dropped everything to follow us about, help us in our inscrutable business of chasing butterflies and netting small, inedible fish, and we all laughed together in uncomprehending mirth. By dimly sensed nationality they were doubtless Costa Ricans; to us they were Everyman. So we think of the jolly people of Uvita as shipping vitamin-filled banana flour to carry to less fortunate, more anemic folk some of the vitality of their little cosmos, while to visiting scientists they gave direct infusions of friendliness. (Frontispiece.)

At noon on the fourth of March we waved good-by to Uvita, and at ten the next morning entered the great Gulf of Dulce. Like the lower Amazon River, its size precluded all intimate interest, and we kept on to a side opening which led into a round paradise of a place called Golfito. It was diversified, solid with tropical jungle and, except for the exigencies of such trivial things as time, money, supplies and the generosity of our patron, we would still be there, quite busy and content. As it was, we spent the best part of a week out of our lives, a week of reawakened memories of sights, sounds and smells. A quarter century of exploration in neotropical jungles has made the wild life more real to me than any sporadic adventures and experiences of civilization. But no choate record or writing can emerge from such exclamations as, "Oh, by Jove, that's an antbird!" or "Listen, there's the first bellbird I've heard for twenty years!" and so on. But there seemed no end to it, and I knew that in yielding myself to these sensuous high lights I was missing a host of small vital beings and happenings.

A cure for this subconscious disregard of the familiar was worked for me by our enthusiastic physician, Eric Liljencrantz. In his own capacity he was talented and competent. As regards wild life in the jungle, a paretic Esquimo could have given him points. To walk slowly along the trails of Golfito and be reinfected with his primordial enthusiasm and appreciation of the strange and beautiful creatures on the ground, in trees and air was a liberal re-education, and to attempt to answer his questions was worse than anything I have ever experienced on "Information, Please."

His ideas of the laws of physics were considerably modified when we stopped by a pool caused by the spreading out of a jungle stream, which in its usual course meandered slowly over logs and pebbles in the shadow of the great trees. A small lizard clung to a dead stick over the water and watched our approach with quick turns of his bright eyes, but no apparent fear. Eric's hand came slowly down in readiness for a quick grasp, when the lizard leaped into the water almost faster than our eyes could follow, and fled with ever-increasing speed across the pool.

It was hardly necessary for Eric to put his thoughts into words: "Why, he didn't sink! He walked on the water!"

Two more followed, obliquely, but fairly upright, little forearms held closely to their breast, and long tail high in a curve, moving so much faster than other creatures can that they sank no deeper than the bases of their long, slender toes. These lizards were four or five inches long, but farther on an eight-incher managed fifteen feet of water without wetting more than his hind legs and tail.

The last to perform was much smaller, but he got away to a bad start and after a few feet began to sink, swimming with only his head out. As I approached he dived, let all his limbs trail and progressed with sinuous movements of body and tail. He vanished beneath a stone in a mass of green algae. We watched, and two minutes later he rose groggily to the surface, and offered no opposition to being caught. These little dynamos got their energy from spiders and spiny ants, with now and then a fresh-water shrimp taken on their underwater trips.

The power to work these water-walking miracles ceased with the slightly larger individuals. They started out bravely, but sank at once. They reminded me of middle-aged, paunchy fathers showing their offspring how they used to be Wows at running bases. Full-grown lizards, a yard in length, made no attempt to run, but dived at once and swam skillfully. Their name, both technically and in the vernacular, is Basilisk, and an old male with roughened scales, reddish eyes, and great irregular head casque, well merits the reference to that fearful medieval monster, whose breath and glance were fatal to human beings. The over-development of the hind legs is of use even after their infantile aquatic peripatetics, for throughout life these lizards are capable of great leaps and bounds, like some of the ancient dinosaurs, and when a straightaway offers itself, they emulate birds and man, and again dinosaurs, and become bipeds, running swiftly on hind legs alone, arms and tail high off the ground.

While Eric was still marveling at the water feat, I called his attention to a crowd of water skaters, rowing about upon the pool in their little regattas of life, their legs only just dimpling the surface film, as we might walk over a thickly stuffed quilt. Size and weight make a lot of difference in the physics of our world, even relative differences, as we can easily see if we drop a mouse, a cat and an elephant off a high tower. As I told Eric, if he will just get me a tower and an elephant I will prove what I mean.

The first evening at Golfito, when we went out on deck a little before seven for dinner, it seemed unusually dark, and in a few minutes the rain, tropical rain, came down in torrents. It was the first of the whole trip and it set all my long latent mental reactions into full play. Were the laboratory windows closed? (In my air-conditioned cabin there was only a single, sealed porthole!) What had been left out? (A glance around showed only several pairs of salt-encrusted sneakers, to which rain was a gift from heaven!), etc. The rain fell as it can fall only in the tropics, straight and windless, then died out in a mist. I did not need the crepuscular voices of the tinamous and the giant toads from the shore to emphasize our latitude.

Early next morning the yelping of toucans excited us before we got halfway to shore. Winding through a shallow barrier of mangroves, we found a busy world of early feeders, herons, sandpipers, silverbeak tanagers, bright rufous squirrels (as unbelievable to a gray squirrel as a panda to a raccoon) and kiskadees. Then a black cat, like an elongate puma, flowed along the curved roots—a jaguarondi. As we landed, macaws and orchids complemented each other, equal in gorgeous colours, one shattering the air with startling cries, the other spraying perfume to such a distance that it was a miracle in the hot, breathless air.

"Why are the huge leaves of that vine filled with slots and holes?" asked our doctor. "That," said I, "is the hurricane plant, and after a great storm that vine will be the only thing left alive, because the force of the wind is broken by filtering through the openings—no, never mind writing it down; that's a joke; go pick up that wasp."

"One joke at a time is enough," retorted Eric. So I went over and picked up the wasp myself and handed it to my friend. It was wicked looking, from the trembling, nervous antennae to the gauzy wings, the yellow bands on the abdomen, and the quivering, pointed sting. When we put the insect in a vial and examined it under a hand lens, the antennae were still more wasp-like than anything else, but the wings, instead of being divided by an intricate network of horny lines, were reticulated by lines of minute scales; the head and body were not hard, smooth armour, but covered with minute, feathery scales, and the sting, instead of being an intricate poison apparatus, was a slender bundle of harmless hairs. But even this wasp impersonator could not quite alter the shape of its body and produce a suitable wasp-waist, but its guardian Master of Mimicry had dipped his brush in dark pigment, drew a broad band of black shadow across the base of the abdomen, and behold! the wasp-waist. Colour, antennae, abdomen, wings, even every movement—a quick, jerky walk, a nervous curving around of the sting—all were those of a dangerous yellow

254

28. *Gulf of Dulce, Costa Rica.* The full grandeur of the tropical jungle of Golfito.

jacket. Yet this insect came from a caterpillar, not a grub, and it was wholly and altogether a perfectly good moth.

The incredible marvel of this mimicry slowly filled Eric's consciousness, and I was glad that we both stood for a long time, looking and wondering in silence. Vocal exclamations are often only under-appreciations. We were lucky to have this one of our first jungle finds, for it so aptly illustrated the terrific struggle for life here, compared with the easier tension among the lesser census of wild creatures of temperate and northern lands. Not a niche must be left unfilled, not a trick or artifice unattempted in the evolution of jungle existence.

The trail was rough but wide and fairly clear, and it was different from any other jungle trail I had ever seen—it was straight, impossibly straight. The explanation came later from a young American engineer who told us that it was the first rough survey line for a United Fruit narrow-gauge railway. It would some day receive bananas from great (present blue-print) plantations in Golfito and carry them straight through the jungle, over two low ranges into the next bay to the south, which is in Panama. So the wonders of this jungle became all the more precious, because so soon they would be thinned out and frightened, and in place of great trees and lovely orchids and birds there would be men and dogs, bananas and paydays. Ultimately, some men, somewhere, would be able to deposit large sums of money in their banks, but they would never know or care how much more attractive and scenic were macaws and jungle lilies than chickens and miles of banana plants, how infinitely sweeter the voices of tinamous and wild pigeons, than the barking of curs and the roar of outboard motors. But if I keep this up I shall dissolve into sen-

29. *The Amazing Mimics of Golfito Jungle.* A harmless moth is almost indistinguishable from a stinging wasp.

timentality, and weep into my journal! So I shall return to Eric and the jungle as it was on this sixth day of March.

The first half-mile along this trail showed all the typical characters of a tropical jungle. Whether in the lowlands of British Guiana, or the hinterland of Brazil, in the African Congo, the hot, steamy, leech-ridden forests of the Malay States and Borneo, or here, at sea level, on the coast of southern Costa Rica, the same general description applies. A few yards along the trail there loomed a tree trunk, yards around. The bark was utterly hidden beneath tassels of moss and mosaics of lichens. Up and up our eyes followed the mighty bole, straight and free from limbs, until high in space, yards and yards above the topmost twig of our northern forests, the first limbs appeared. Small insects, perhaps little butterflies, flew about up there, until our glasses changed them into good-sized birds. It was like looking down from a plane at the sea from a mile or more, and suddenly have the distance made real by the lazy crawling of a tiny ship—actually a large freighter.

Twenty-five yards beyond the first great tree another appeared, this one smooth and clean, with graceful buttresses flowing, winding far out from the trunk, thin and soft-looking as the folds in a daguerreotype of our grandmother's bridal train. The tops of these jungle giants spread so wide, and intercepted so much sunshine, that only saplings and weaker growths could thrive between. The comparison of a jungle with a cathedral is often apt—the enormous, bare columns, the quiet, the oblique, coloured shafts of light reaching through the lofty, emerald sky windows down to the very floor. But the simile of cathedraled aisles may sometimes become confused, for abruptly, in the course of our walk, from the highest aerial foliage to the lowliest growths there appeared a network of streamers, vines, living strands and lianas, sometimes gay with orchids and air plants, often tangled and looped like the rigging of a wrecked ship.

Luck was with us, for soon we came to a place where the undeviating necessity of the trail had compelled the cutting straight through upper trunk and limbs of a mighty fallen tree. I could safely prophesy that here the curtain would go up for us on one of the most dramatic, affecting jungle episodes: the prologue, the smashing, catastrophic fall of the giant tree, with act succeeding act, scaled down to the patient, ultra slow-motion tempo of plant growth.

I led Eric down the long length of trunk, horizontal, but poised on roots and branches ten feet above the ground. Finally we reached the great mass of upturned roots. The tree had fallen a few months before, and the wide clearing thus exposed to the sun had already begun its regular botanical evolution, that unvarying sequence so familiar to me.

Almost like the quick reaction of a host of little animals, unnumbered tiny plants, daisy-like, had awakened from their long seed sleep, flung wide their leaves and burst into thousands of blossoms. We do not know how their seeds ever reached this place, or how long they had aestivated in the uncongenial dusk of the jungle floor. Now they were having their brief carnival of life, hastening to ripen their seeds for another generation. But even as their petals fell, the second line of vegetation rushed into the unexpected gap, the small island of light in the dark sea of the jungle. This was an unlovely blitz, a tangle of low, thorny vines, terrible saw-edged razor-grass, soft-wooded, swift-growing spiny brush, forming chevaux-de-frise wholly impenetrable to two- and four-legged creatures of any size.

But even on the day of the fall, other plants had sensed the change, and what had been weak, spindly little saplings felt their sap assume new speed, acquire more abundant nourishment; the offspring of the tree itself, and those of neighbouring giants began in turn their battle for life, the only chance they would ever have. There was no mercy, no brotherly aid; it was each for himself, a contest, not of weeks or months, but of decades and perhaps centuries, before some one plant, stronger by heredity, or exact situation, or whatever we in our ignorance call luck, before some single tree would win through, reaching up and out, killing all competitors. And unless it, in turn, was felled and burned to provide us with sliced bananas for breakfast, our Nth great-grandchildren could stand at its base, look up and up, and, I hope, wonder and marvel as we were doing today.

I had, professor-wise, poured out this account for Eric's benefit, and then we crept through the tangle of great roots, like maggots through cheese, though less skillfully, and to our delight found, here and there, the beginnings of spiny vines sprouting through the blossoms, and several of what appeared to be seedling trees.

When we returned to the trail, even after our exertions, we were not unpleasantly overheated, and this made patent another jungle character. In the sun outside, the thermometer had probably risen to 125° or thereabouts, while among the trees it was 78°. On the water of Golfito the glare was intense, but here we were surrounded by a cool, diffused twilight, and the universal greenness was sheer eye balm. In some of the semi-desert bays to the north, sandflies and ticks made life almost unbearable, while here, as in so many other tropical jungles, we were troubled by no biting insects or other creatures, except for the usual quota of bête rouge if we insisted on sitting for long on inviting mossy logs, or lying at length on the soft jungle floor.

One thing is certain, no one can walk for long through a jungle and remain conceited. The Lord-of-Creation no longer strides over hills and plains, or up mountains. Exactly as an ant creeps over the ground in a field of grain three feet in height, so we must trudge slowly and silently in the dim, cool shadows of these great growths, listening to strange sounds, sniffing odours from unknown sources. I know of no better cure for human vanity.

My physician-pupil, as we explored the Golfito jungle day after day, fairly boiled with excitement and wonder. He was not "Eric, or Little by Little," but "Eric, or Leaps and Bounds!" in his avid curiosity. It was interesting to see him forming wrong conclusions about the animal life, logical conclusions based on superficial observations, and reasonable theories founded on apparent truths; all exactly the same as I had developed and believed in at one time. I watched the old magician of Nature forcing cards on Eric, who accepted them without question and believed implicitly in the results.

In the course of our walks, great bees, appearing enormous in the dim light, roared past like bombers going all out, carpenter bees, giving an anticlimactic slant to our simile, for they were laden with nonexplosive pollen. Two-inch wasps with emerald bodies and wings like living claret flew slowly, searching with diabolical thoroughness for equally gigantic tarantula spiders. A beetle, harlequined in mustard-yellow and gray, crept up a palm with forelegs half a foot long. All this and more Eric saw, and from his lips burst a law: "Jungle Life is Gigantic." This I shattered by telling him of the thousands upon thousands of minute bees and wasps and beetles hidden everywhere about us. The giants were, by their size, forced upon his notice, but he might spend another two weeks and not come across another titan of its kind.

I saw his eyes fixed upon a leafy bush, and presently he walked over and looked down at a katydid on a leaf, sprawled out, motionless, a super-katydid with wings, each of which had an expanse of at least four square inches. Eric knew katydids, so with a quick grasp he picked up this one, and with equal celerity dropped it, his hand dripping blood. Two strong jaws had sunk deep into his thumb and double lines of serried leg spines raked his fingers. If the song of this insect was up to its armament of pointed forceps and toothed rasps, it must sound like a buzz saw.

"In spite of all you've told me," said Eric, nursing his wounds, "I still hold to the gigantic idea.

"At least," he added, "I can safely say that most tropical creatures are brilliantly coloured."

"You can say it, but unfortunately it is far from true," I answered, becoming stuffily pedantic. "If we credit Costa Rica with eight hundred species of birds, the number of dull-coloured forms is greatly in excess over those with bright feathers. There are seventy gorgeously coloured parrots and humming-birds, but there are also seventy antbirds and woodhewers alone, to mention only two Quaker-hued jungle families, and

260

so on. Toucans and trogons flash across the glades in front of you, but tinamous, doves and wrens are almost unnoticed."

Eric clung fast to two other aphorisms, which I made no effort to debunk. These were, that tropical jungles are filled with creatures which are not what they seem, and others which appear to be what they are not. This Alice in Wonderland tangle he hugged to himself and enjoyed it as much as I always have and always shall.

"A woodpecker at last," said Eric, as a slender, chocolate-coloured bird hitched up a tree trunk. This was a case where the value of a bird is doubled in the hand, so I shot it. In structure of beak and stiffened, prop-like tail feathers it was woodpecker, but with its three toes in front and one behind, it hopped several rungs up the avian ladder of evolution, and took its place with the superior Passeriformes, together with swallows and nightingales. The only thing wrong with the bird was its human handle—woodhewer. The members of this group are peckers and tappers and knockers on wood, but in no sense hewers; that name should be applied to what we call woodpeckers, with their strong, hammer-like bills, built for hewing and banging on tree trunks, and even tunneling into them.

As we entered a small clearing, a sudden hissing and a loud swishing of wings marked the hasty flight of three black vultures which flapped heavily up through the branches. We found they had been feeding on a dead capuchin monkey, like those we had seen and chattered with a quarter of a mile back; jet-black little chaps with amber-coloured face and chest. As I was leaving the clearing I saw a stray bit of monkey flesh caught on a palm frond, apparently disgorged by the vultures in their haste. A movement on it drew my attention, and I saw walking over it a bluebottle fly of sorts, and as she walked, she sowed (there is no other word) a line of living maggots over the meat—so keen is competition here, with such speed is every opportunity seized.

Eric called me back and pointed to a high limb. There in full view, but until now invisible to us, was a king vulture, *el Rey de los Zopilotes* as the natives call him, hunched up, watching us. The glasses showed his clean, ivory plumage, the brilliancy of the yellow and red wattles on head and neck, and the unwinking, dead-white eyes, those amazing organs which can become telescopic or myopic at will.

"Even the vultures are coloured like hummingbirds," said Eric, reverting to our earlier argument.

"Yes, but he was feeding with three black ones, so the dull plumages still have it, three hundred per cent."

Not long afterward George Swanson, our artist, called us to see a cluster of seven butterfly chrysalids hanging from the underside of a leaf. They were cellophane-clear, and the yellow and black wings of embryo Heliconia butterflies could be seen through them. But we had to look quickly, for they were hatching while we waited. One was already out, but still clinging to the frayed-out ghost of its home, its wings soft, swollen, diminutive blobs of pigment. While we watched, breathless, a butterfly of the same species fluttered up, and with no hesitation flew directly to the still swathed, newly emerged one, and instantly mated with it. Here was a female two minutes out of its chrysalid, while her mate had wings tattered and torn, dull of luster, evidently near the end of his short jungle existence. In the glade we had seen death

262

made the most of, exploited by vultures and flies; here, birth, or shall we say resurrection, played its instantaneous part in preparation for future generations.

As we reached the edge of the jungle, a monstrous insect, a huge scarlet and black grasshopper, rose with a whirr of wings and landed with a plop! on the front of my shirt. He took off before I could seize him, fluttered down the beach and fell into the water close to shore. This strange performance on the part of such a strong-winged flier demanded investigation and I scooped him up in a net, and put him swiftly to sleep in the killing jar. Later examination showed no defect in his body armour, antennae and legs all accounted for, wings— spreading full nine inches—in perfect condition. When his body was dissected, however, not only was his aerial disability explained, but the wonder aroused that he could move at all, or was alive. In place of whatever organs function in a grass- hopper's torso, there were fourteen large pupa cases of some kind of bluebottle fly, all ready to hatch, with round, black eyes plainly visible, waiting to record impressions as soon as they could emerge from their present home in the fuselage of this living biplane. And I, a detached onlooker, knew not what to call evil, what good. Meditation on this single hap- pening, involving fifteen living creatures, from the points of view of flies, or grasshopper or myself, left the mind in a whirl of conflicting emotions. And the problem was rendered no simpler by the frustration of all possibility of success—the accidental interruption by myself of an excellent meal for some hungry fish.

On my last day in Golfito I went alone far into the jungle and settled down for observation at the edge of a marsh, where the stream sank into the soggy, mossy ground. While I was getting comfortable, a circle of little red-clawed crabs nervously *heiled* to me with their pincers held aloft, as they sidled and backed away from my vicinity.

For ten minutes I was completely baffled by a penetrating call-note, perfect in its ventriloquial character. After I had made many attempts at translation into human speech, one word only satisfied me, *Dough!* It came from every direction (*Dough!*) including straight overhead (*Dough!*) or whatever direction I happened to be looking (*Dough!*). I finally decided that its slight, bell-like quality was that of some small frog. Then another note came to my ears, quite as ethereal and indefinite as to direction. This was a very sweet trill, with a delicate, tender cadence. It had much of the character of a phrase of the evening song of a wood thrush or veery. Several manakins came and went, twice drinking at the small stream, and suddenly I got my binoculars on a splendid chestnut-sided warbler in full spring plumage. I watched it fly-catching for many minutes, and wondered if, six weeks from now, I might not see this selfsame bird near New York City.

I swept the surrounding jungle with my glasses and noticed, from time to time, a blur at one spot. Careful focusing at last showed me that I was looking at the courtship dance of a long-tailed manakin. These are delightful little, chunky birds, almost all black except for azure-blue back, crimson crest and bright orange legs and feet.

I crawled a few yards nearer, until I had a clear view. There were three males and a single leaf-green female. She sat very quietly and watched the proceedings without much apparent interest, while two of the male birds almost tore themselves apart for her. One at a time, they flew to a short, bare, horizontal twig, about two feet in length, and instantly began a jumping-jack performance. From one end of the twig the bird bounced into the air, in an oblique arc which landed it at the farther end, whence it instantly took off again. Its wings vibrated in a fluttering blur, and it uttered a drawn-out *Chuuuuuuuuuuuuwe! Chuuuuuuuuuuuuwe! Chuuuuuuuuuuuuwe!* This sound strongly recalled the whip-like note of a towhee. Each utterance was perfectly synchronized with one performance—bounce, aerial arc, and drop, bounce, aerial arc, and drop. There was not the slightest hesitation between the landing and the take-off—it really gave the appearance of a bouncing rubber ball—and the completed turn consumed just one second of time. The first bird bounced twelve times in exactly as many seconds. The second bird then took the place of the first, bounced eighteen times, and vanished. Instantly the first bird resumed his performance, and after eight bounces flew up close to the female. They sat quietly about an inch apart, and at once began a duet, revealing the source of the ventriloquial bell note which I had accredited to an amphibian.

The duet was absurdly simple, but melodious, the silly word *Dough!* being invested by the birds with an infinite sweetness and liquid quality. Again and again the sequence was the same, twenty or thirty times, and always as follows: the female would say *Dough!* and the male instantly responded with *Dough-e!* or *Dough-e-dough!* After the first two, the syllables merged, the female coming in on every first *Dough,* but never uttering the two- or three-syllabled phrase. These were purely the masculine part.

Finally, to my surprise, the thrush-like call came from near at hand, several times, and I found that the third male, who had not danced, but only sat quietly a short distance away and overhead, was singing this third utterance, over and over, to himself. After several more minutes my cramped muscles demanded a slight shift, and with the movement, every manakin vanished.

This courtship has been described in part several times, but with a lack of exact detail. The *Dough-e-dough* phrase has provided the native name in several Central American countries, written *Toledo*. The point of especial interest to me was the use of the same courting twig by two males in succession. Usually birds which have such elaborate courtships maintain a strictly individual domain or territory.

This manakin episode was a satisfying finale to our week in the Golfito jungle. As the Zaca slowly made her way out into the larger gulf, I looked back and saw as yet no visible man-made change. It was exactly as the present Indians and their ancestors had always known it. And it was also the unaltered home of those other natives, whose lives are lost in antiquity. Our only knowledge of them is of the dust of the men and the women lying in the innumerable graves scattered throughout the jungle, each individual provided with adequate and beautifully decorated pottery, and each with a charm of pure, soft gold, some quaintly fashioned *huaca* of a bird or a frog or a little, staring idol.

CHAPTER XXII

DANCING FIDDLERS
(with Jocelyn Crane)

TO our eyes, even after all the string of bays we had explored along the two thousand miles of Pacific coastline, Bahia Honda seemed almost the loveliest, and for our work most satisfying—roomy, but not too large, landlocked, with hills on all sides heavily wooded, fresh-water streams flowing slowly into the sea, a shore line variegated with beaches of pure white and of black lava sand, and rocks at the entrance cupping great, intermittent tidepools.

Others shared our opinion of its beauty, for within a week two great yachts entered this northern Panama Bay and anchored, William K. Vanderbilt's *Alva* and Hugh Chisholm's *Aras*. It was a rare sight in this little-known, distant bay, inhabited by only a handful of malaria-ridden natives, to see three such vessels, a trio of four-lettered yachts, *Alva*, *Aras* and *Zaca*.

Our first night light was a revelation of fear. A host of larval anchovies, virile silver threads held prisoner by the unaccustomed glare, little by little fell into a hypnotic routine, anti-clockwise, around and around. Then some, to them, monster fish would dash in and snatch here and there, turning the shimmering mass into a tangle of terror—too much drawn by the light to leave, too frightened to swim alongside their fellows. Fishes are forever dumb—voice, eyelids, mobility of mouth, eloquence of hands, all are denied them. But when we turned off the light, and blackness again closed down over the zone of watery fear, there came from the distant shore what seemed a vocal expression of the hopelessness of life for nine out of ten of all infant fish, a wail full of sorrow, of despairing lament, the voice of the giant goatsucker, well-named Poor-me-all-alone. And I went to sleep with this pleasantly sorrowful, wholly anthropomorphic thought! At dawn, however, I was awakened by an antithetical bird voice, the virile, ringing, cheerful *Hánaqua! Hánaqua! Hánaqua!* of the small, brown tree fowl.

We went, by instinct, first to a long, sandy beach which turned out to be our favourite studying and collecting place throughout the week of our stay. The sand was soft and white, and the trees, beyond high tide, typical of the jungle, with graceful, widespreading, buttressed trunks. Coconut palms leaned far forward over the beach, but kept their ball of roots tight in firmer soil, and everywhere the colour and scent of frangipanni blossoms drew and satisfied a host of bees and butterflies. We dug in at a place where roots were desks and tables, and sand was sheer seating comfort. Here we unlimbered our recording outfit—notebooks, pencils, glasses, dividers, vials, jars, pails, nets and guns. (Plate 30.)

Very soon we realized that there were far more butterflies than any amount of frangipanni could attract, and then we saw they were all going in one direction, blown along by no wind, but irrevocably more so by the impelling force of instinct. Throughout our stay, for at least one week out of this March month, hundreds, and tens of thousands of butterflies, orange and white, fluttered southeastwardly, some with swift, undeviating progress, but most of them sauntering slowly, even reluctantly, almost but never quite alighting. *Catopsilias* they were, whose kin I have seen migrating in similar swarms a continent's width away. Now and then an individual of some other species, even an opalescent, day-flying moth, would join them, as a floating leaf is whirled for a moment in the eddy of a stream. But the fateful force held them lightly, theirs was an ephemeral bondage, and a blossom, or another of their own kind, was sufficient to break the spell.

Hummingbirds hummed behind us, great wine-coloured doves boomed, toucans yelped, and antbirds crescendoed, to use silly, man-made words for these wonderful tropical sounds. Once, we heard a scratching of claws on wood, and small, shrill squeaks, and a family of five coatimundis ran, like long-tailed little bears, along the lower branches. Frigatebirds drifted past and pelicans looked down upon us, but for the most part we were alone with the thin storm of butterflies and the ghost crabs that raced across the sand.

Butterflies, hummingbirds, coatis—all these were comparatively new organisms to us. And then my ears caught a delicate clashing and tinkling somewhat like a brook dashing against the hardened water of ice and icicles. Suspiciously I turned my head, hoping against hope. But no! A shell rolled down the slope I had excavated for my feet, and I saw it animated by proxy of a hermit which, like Morrobie Jukes, had tumbled over the rim of the pit. I did not want to see or watch or write about hermits again. Like the poor, they were with us always on all beaches, but I found myself watching, in spite of myself, just as one's eyes leave performing horses or a trapeze acrobat and turn to superlative clowns. For that is what hermits always seem to me, although I was soon to be reminded that, besides being amusing, the activities of these creatures were often prompted by stark tragedy, with concomitants of life and death.

I watched one which was dragging a murex shell covered with sharp spines and ridges. It often got out of control and rolled over once or twice from its very unwieldiness. There were two sharply marked subsequent reactions. If the upset was an accident, no matter how buffeting and rough, the crab emerged at once. But if the passing shadow of my hand played over it, the crab remained immured for a minute or more. His sense organs provided an excellent connection between him and his environment. His eyes, on the end of long, mobile stalks, never ceased their vigil; his front antennae, consisting of threadlike stems with thickened end segments, played tremulously upon the air, forever striving for perception of the invisible floating particles which we call the sense of smell. And finally, the filamentous second pair of antennae attended to more material information, touching and playing upon, and examining for good or ill, every stone or shell or whatever the scrambling legs brought within reach. (Plate 31.)

At lunch time hundreds of the hermits formed a dense ring of kibitzers around our resting place. A kitchen midden of crusts and empty sardine tins became a Mecca for crowds of mobile mollusk shells. I watched carefully, and all comparison with comedy and buffoonery passed, as I saw developing a battle royal. When one hermit fell into a little pool of sardine oil, he instantly became the focus of attack on the part

270

30. *Bahia Honda, Panama.* The beach of the painted ghost crabs.

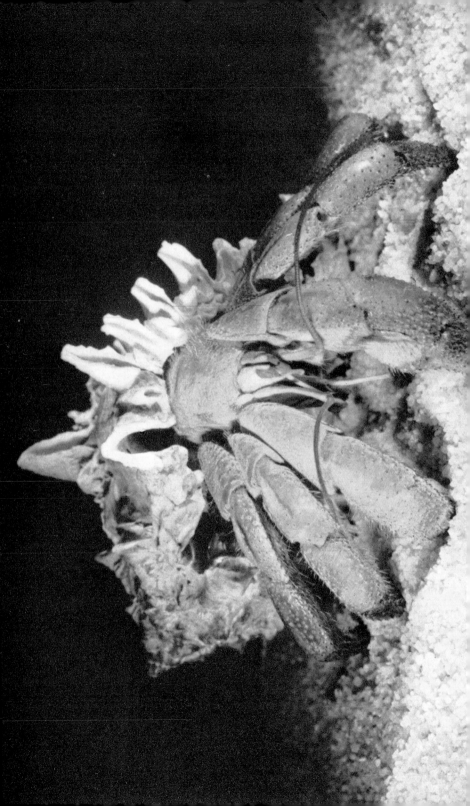

of all his fellows. They piled on him, and rolled him about, and sooner or later, when for an instant he loosened his grip on his castle, they dragged him forth and devoured him. Brotherly love must be but a thin veneer when a dash of salad dressing will turn a fellow hermit into an appetizing entrée.

Whenever I approached a solitary hermit crab, his reaction was exactly that of a football player who, running with the ball, when tackled tears himself free and rolls over and over. The simile was exact as my approaching shadow impelled the little being to shut himself up, the impetus of his advance being transferred to his spherical home. Twice (to change my simile) I have seen a hermit crab hole himself in one, as he began his rolling near the open tunnel of a ghost crab.

The tide was going down and the lower part of the beach was dotted with an increasing multitude of little painted ghost crabs, all busily feeding. Suddenly, twenty feet away in an empty space of sand, a grandfather of a crab appeared like a card in a magician's hand, and before we had completed an inane "Oh, look!" with an equally silly gesture, the crab—was not. Whether he had vanished into thin air or thicker sand, the eye could not say. Ten minutes later he re-emerged from the heart of the beach, and this time we could see beside him the neat, two-inch opening to his tunnel, in which he had passed the flood-time of high tide. He was still sporting the camouflage of a sleepy mien and encrusting sand, but when certain that no tree would again point at him, he began a carcinological strip tease. Some day we will get a colour movie of this, but until then we can only make use of opaque words, distorting phrases.

He was gray, bedraggled, sand-smirched, like the White

271

31. A *Hermit Crab*. The comedian and the villain of the beaches.

Knight after tumbling into a sandy mire. Little by little, as the warm sun dried his clothing of sand grains, with his capable hands and mouth-parts he began to clean and expose the various plates of his armour, from back and eyestalks to dactyl octet. Probably a crab has never before been compared with a sunset, but here goes: His back and legs glowed with coral red, touched with gold and rufous; the eyestalks showed soft tints of pink, with the lighthouse-like lenses pale gray; and above all rose the eye wires like prosaic lightning rods, but, unlike them, flame colour. The stalks sank into sockets of yellow gold, his underparts were crimson, his toes warm buff, and his "hands" had light gold palms and pincer-fingers of coral. Rubbing his palms together as if in self-appreciation of a cleaning job well done, or perhaps in anticipation of an excellent breakfast, he sedately made his way toward the damp sand near the edge of the water. When the nearest of his fellows, who were feeding in hundreds on the fresh-wet sand, were only a few feet away, he seemed suddenly to become aware of the splendid feast before him. Casting decorum to the winds, he stretched to tiptoe and raced waterward with feather-light speed until he reached a vacant spot at the very edge of the tide. Then he fell to the day's real work of sifting from the sand microscopic manna washed up by the tide, and turning the tiny particles into that complex piece of protoplasm which is a Painted Ghost Crab.

From that moment until the tide chased them toward their holes, he and his fellows never ceased their feeding, and to what magnificent simplicity have they reduced this troublesome phase of life! They simply walked over an interminable expanse of what might well have been oatmeal or other cereal.

Raising these "spoon vittles" to their mouths with alternate, scooping claws, they mumbled and sifted and spat out the residue sand in the shape of neat, oval pills which lay on the sand, conspicuously set off by their black shadows. As the crabs sidled slowly along, their rejected pellets gradually formed great curves and lines, decorating the whole beach with interesting dietetic patterns. Their gustatory rhythm was four scoops and a gob to the second, and they seemed blissfully to enjoy this feeding on safari. As we watched them, I remembered certain dishes of spinach whose gritty, arenaceous content had set my teeth on edge, and I readily admitted that in definite respects crabs are infinitely superior to man.

The ghost crabs of Honda were proving to be among the most pleasant crustaceans we found down the length of Middle America. All crabs challenged our scientific sleuthing in one way or another: the great swimmers and spiders that came up in the deep dredges from the bottom of the sea, the daddy-long-legs-like arrow crabs climbing over seaweed in the bays, the agile Sally Lightfoots of the rocks, the scarlet and black trapezias that called the coral reefs home, the hundred and one kinds lurking under stones by the shore, and, above all, the fiddlers which haunted the mud of the mangroves. Here, with the ghost crabs, we could sit at ease with only the trouble of holding our binoculars steady, and they came and performed before us. But with the other crabs it was far different. The human frame was often strained to its utmost.

The crabs caught in the deep-sea dredges had to be roughly identified, described as to colours, recorded, labeled and preserved—along with all the starfish, shrimps, shells and fish which came up with them—as fast as possible, before a new avalanche of creatures from a succeeding haul buried the sorting trays. Coral crabs must be literally hammered out of their hiding places, after the great amber masses had been brought up by a helmeted diver and piled on deck; small towers and castles were laboriously cracked, and every stony labyrinth explored by our giants' fingers, for clinging crabs which would rather sacrifice several legs than loose their holds. Even then, once we got them out, there was little chance of learning anything of their habits, before preserving them in vials of alcohol; coral crabs, dredged crabs and those that existed under stones as well all lived lives discouragingly secret to curious scientists.

When we hunted the crabs of the mangrove mud, a wholly different technique was needed which required a peculiarly sticky kind of persistence. After we had gained experience, we never even tried to catch a rare specimen with a shovel, because as we dug so many neighbouring crab holes opened up in the midst of our constantly incaving excavation that our prey readily escaped unseen—if we missed cutting him in two by mistake. Therefore, every large, rare crab was hunted simply with a trowel and two hands. Although the chase always started decorously enough, with business-like scoops of the trowel, by the time the crab was actually seized the mud resembled a bomb crater complete with casualty: the struggling collector was always stretched at full length, literally biting the mud, his arm plunged in up to the shoulder, while his fingers timorously clutched a slippery mass of shell, legs and giant nippers. When crab and fingers eventually emerged, we were not always certain whether we were catching crabs or the crabs catching us.

While all the little armoured creatures were our special concern, it was these mud-loving fiddlers which were the most fun and yielded the most surprises of all. Around the corner from Ghost Crab Beach at Honda, on the shore of the inner part of the bay, a great expanse of sandy mud lay exposed at low tide. In the midst of it lay a fiddler metropolis. Looking at it from a distance, we were aware of many, little circling pink creatures, all in motion, in actual circles, or back and forth. These were the males, while among them were the dull brown females and young. If we sat or lay motionless on the flat, the crabs soon lost all fear, re-emerged from their holes in every direction and began to carry on their delightful activities.

Day after day, as we watched fiddlers digging, eating, dueling and courting along the edges of one tropical bay after another, it had become increasingly difficult to consider them with that beautiful abstraction with which all self-respecting scientists are supposed to observe their non-human companions on this planet. The fact that fiddlers have ten legs instead of two and a hard shell in place of our own assortment of internal bones became of less and less importance, as we learned of their varying personalities and their ingenuity in attaining the ideals of fiddlerdom: food and females.

It was this colony at Honda that gave us our first blaze of inspiration about some of the most exciting secrets of the fiddlers' lives. Seated on the edge of that particular mud flat, we had in view a dozen kinds of fiddler crabs at once, and through the binoculars we could watch every detail of their interminable activities without disturbing the busy creatures in the least. The claw-waving of the male Flame-legged Fiddlers was the most entertaining of all. Females and young, with two tiny claws, were, as usual, an inconspicuous mottled brown, but large males were gay with backs of white and iridescent blue, the eight legs flame-scarlet and the huge fiddling claw a beautiful rose. When scurrying rapidly along, they reminded us of cowboys on horseback at full gallop, that lovely, smooth gait with the bellies almost touching the ground. Held high aloft, as the rodeo riders do their sombreros, the fiddlers brandished at full height the great claw.

Little by little we realized that this rushing to and fro with arm outstretched was only an occasional interlude. We watched a single large male, and found that he spent much of his time standing before his burrow, waving his great claw slowly up and down, or back and forth in a large arc, while his small claw pinched up sand and brought it to his mouth. Here his thousand bristles strained it free of nourishment and passed the rest to the rear, where he periodically wiped off the drooling detritus with a flick of his small nipper, his general table technique being similar to that of the ghost crabs.

Every little while, however, a wave of excitement would sweep over him and his masculine neighbours, who would all leave their lunch without a qualm and go racing about on tiptoe, with the great pink claws extended stiffly, and their small claws spread just as stiffly in the opposite direction, their whole attitude being one of alertness and intense excitement.

At last it dawned on us that this behaviour was only induced by the appearance of a female, so small and drab and inconspicuous that at first she escaped our notice. To the males, however, she was the acme of interest, if only she were of adequate age, yet unburdened by eggs, and if she at least had definitely stopped eating for a moment and hence was open to persuasion. Even more desirable, apparently, were foot-loose flirts who provocatively wandered far from their holes, electrifying every male they passed. When a male succeeded in getting close to one of these, he would literally dance her along in the circle of his great nipper-arm, never touching her, but trying to tease her over to his hole. A female never seemed frightened when thus captured, nor on the other hand did she miss an opportunity to duck out from under and escape.

We did not see a single male succeed in winning a mate by this method, which really seemed more a sport than serious flowers-and-candy courtship, and suddenly we realized it was the exact carcinological counterpart of that giddy Panamanian carnival dance, the tamborito, in which the woman dances first with one man, then with a succession of others. Each partner performs with his right arm, hat in hand, extended in only the slightest curve about the girl, not touching her, while his feet do intricate steps and she pretends to struggle to escape, as the drums beat out a haunting rhythm. At Honda, the great woodpeckers, the bellbirds, quadrillebirds and the giant jungle cicadas furnished the fiddlers' accompaniment.

When we shifted our eyes to some dazzling white midgets whose colony lay farther out in the mud, we saw that the rhythm of their waving was entirely different from that of the Flame-legs. Furthermore, they never chased females, but bounced endlessly in one spot, jerking the great claw with

277

frantic gusto up and down whenever they succeeded in capturing a trace of feminine interest; surely they were the original jitterbugs. A third group of dancers, clad in magenta and gray, would have done credit to the Russian ballet, spreading both nippers outward in a slow and gracious gesture, as they rose to tiptoe and danced feather-light steps from side to side. Their resemblance to finished toe dancers was delightfully close, and not even Pavlova, could she have shrunk to proper size, would have considered any one beneath her as a partner. At last we saw the truth: Each species was doing its own courtship dance, which differed as greatly as rumbas from waltzes, and each performance was as characteristic and as much a part of courtship as the song of a robin, the display of a peacock, or the springtime serenade of a frog. So distinct were the dances that we could recognize different forms in a mixed colony as far as we could see their motions, just as you can tell a hermit thrush from a veery by his song alone.

No sooner had we settled the dancing question to our satisfaction than another truth was plain. Seventy-odd years ago, Fritz Müller watched a little Brazilian fiddler change into a brilliant "wedding costume" when he emerged from his hole into the sunshine. Now, on the shores of Panama, we found that transient courting colours were the rule among fiddlers, and were donned by courting males freshly every day. Like good Latin Americans preparing for fiestas, the crabs literally dressed up before dancing, changing before our eyes from dowdy browns and grays to the rose and white, purple and green or turquoise, magenta and blue of their respective clans.

There was no doubt whatever that the females, once their attention was secured by a prospective mate, were properly

278

impressed. We watched an especially brilliant Emerald-backed Fiddler, which turned out to be a new species. He was in full display colour, and for at least an hour had been trying vainly to attract the attention of a drab little female four inches away. He interrupted display only with the merest minimum of feeding, but she apparently paid no attention at all, redigging her hole and feeding busily, with never a glance in his direction. At last, however, she stopped feeding and appeared to see him for the first time. With this slight encouragement, he speeded up the tempo of his dance, pumping his great purple claw frantically up and down and adding extra clogging steps to the prancing of his eight green legs. The female sidled an inch or two in his direction, pausing for snacks as she came. Her suitor displayed still faster, and at last won her fascinated attention. Almost hypnotized she seemed as she watched, motionless, an inch away. He varied his dance, revolving slowly before her like a mannequin, so that his back of iridescent green faced her alternately with his purple claw. Finally she approached within reach, he stroked her legs gently with his own, and she stroked his in return. They parted, briefly, he did one more prancing jig, and then dashed suddenly down his hole, his bright claw vanishing last with a final, irresistible waggle. And at once the female followed after.

Five minutes later the male reappeared briefly at the mouth of the hole, kicked up a plug of mud, and deftly flipped it over the entrance with his last-projecting legs as a most eloquent "DO NOT DISTURB." And we saw no more of them.

CHAPTER XXIII

SIRENS OF THE DEEP

TWENTY-TWO miles off shore we slowed down and sent out in all directions the emerald beams of the under-water light. Many creatures came to it, but five stood out in diversity and unexpectedness. There was a twelve-inch squid with huge, goggling eyes, each a full inch across, with skin first red, then transparent, dying a translucent, pinkish brown. What looked like a little bat alighted on the deck and proved to be a Galápagos storm petrel, almost the smallest of all seabirds. Then a big cicada whirred on board, and at the same moment, from the restless surface of the water was netted a fish—silvery, round, of the size of a silver dollar, appropriately named thread-fin, for back from its fins there trailed streamers four times as long as its body.

While we were watching it swim round and round a glass dish, there splashed headlong a huge grasshopper, brother to the one we had caught on the Golfito beach. Squid, petrel, cicada, thread-fin and grasshopper—a quintet of unbelievably dissimilar creatures, bound together by only one link, a fateful attraction to the light. The squid and the fish lived in the ocean, the petrel over it, while the insects were strays from the far distant land, their hegira inexplicable on such a calm, clear night. The bird and the grasshopper were both within a half inch of half a foot in length, and all were silent in our company except the cicada which zizzed his way vigorously into the dreamland of chloroform. They brought to mind the nine members of that strange assemblage which came aboard far to the north and four months ago.

Southward and southward we continued, and finally reached familiar Balboa. But our allotted time was not yet up, so with renewed human and diesel fuel we left after forty-eight hours, headed for the mysterious island of Gorgona, off Colombia, almost on the equator. Its life, and its soul—for it has one—are too long to tell of here, and will be another story.

One of the last memories of this second Zaca trip was of the deep-sea fish which came up in our nets, as we again headed for Panama. On April 4th, 1925, I was on the Arcturus, on my first deep-sea expedition. I find in my journal of that day: "In the afternoon, a Petersen trawl was put down to 700 fathoms, and the best haul of the trip was secured." Thirteen years later, on April 4th, 1938, on the Zaca, only a few degrees to the north, I wrote: "Rather heavy swell this morning, but three nets went down to 500 fathoms nicely, and brought up an unusually fine assortment of deep-sea creatures, together with several extraordinary new organisms."

There were grenadiers or rat-tailed macrourids, fish with the heads of cods, and tails which ended in nothing; ever-wonderful ribbons of soft glass waved through our jars, ribbons which some day would have transformed into unknown eels—leptocephalids, we must call them, or else remain silent; a fan-finned, black, nameless wonder of a fish promptly revived in ice-cold salt water, and swam in circles for an hour. Melamphaes, otherwise nameless, also appear, with no light organs but with scales sculptured like a Hindu temple; the everlasting and ever-present round-mouths and lanternfish; silver hatchetfish, never ceasing to stare upward through tubular binoculars of eyes, while all their silver and purple lights shone downward; eels of great vitality, with needle-thin jaws pointing straight forward like those of a heron, others with jaws curving unreasonably far outward, which a Chinese artist might conceivably delineate, but whose practical use is hidden from us. There came up giant scarlet shrimps, seven inches overall, not counting the great extent of antennae—scarlet, we might as well say, from excessive cold, certainly not from boiling; flying snails with tissue shells like cellophane kites and zeppelins, and finally a company of fishing frogfish or anglers, some of which are proving to be new species.

The first of these was, as usual, black as the pit, with ample, sable tailfin, a huge mouth almost splitting the head, and teeth so long that the mouth could never be closed. From the tip of the snout arose a short, thick stalk, luminous all around, topped with a complicated crest, with purplish blue headlight and pale tentacle. From the chin depended a group of bushy barbels, all pale luminous, six stems which branched into knob-tipped tentacles. The eye had a luminous spot on the eyeball which, we should think, would interfere with clear vision. But Nature seems singularly unconcerned with what we think, and goes ahead with pragmatically proved successes. The upper contour of the body was fairly even, but the whole lower half bulged irregularly, hiding some recent, enormous meal.

A second dragon anglerfish was still larger, with three strong fins, a small mouth with a fine, even set of teeth. Here and there, wholly at random, over the head and body, there sprouted strong, sharp spines, some with luminous bases, sprouting anywhere, without any plan or pattern. Bright blue light is very rare among deep-sea fish, but this creature, un-named as yet, quite new to science, had spots of sheer spectrum-blue symmetrically placed, but in unexpected places: in front of the anal fin, and behind both this and the dorsal fin, on one of the anal rays and two of the tail rays. (Plate 32.)

The head luminosity was strange and monstrous in its arrangement. The whole front of the snout and the entire chin were covered with fleshy tubercles, swollen into an outstanding curve, and giving forth intermittent white flashes. An exceedingly stout stem rose up from the head, swelling into a bulb at the summit and from here sending up two thick tentacles, the whole being almost as long as the entire fish. The superstructure was black, dotted with small white lights, and the tentacles were all luminescent. I have never seen such beauty of colour and light blended with such ugliness of form.

The three large nets which I sent down were attached to the wire only a few yards apart, to a depth of five hundred fathoms. Whenever this is done, although the nets are so close together, the catch in each is always remarkably individual. Almost never have I caught many creatures of the same species in all three. But this time, in each of two nets, there came up a fish so exactly like its fellow that they might have been one fish and its shadow. Each one, in fact, was as black as any shadow could be, and the marvel of them made the coincidence all the more spectacular.

They were small anglers, not more than five inches overall,

jet-black except for a remarkable structure on the tip of the head tentacle, so intricate, so lovely in its many parts, that I immediately named it the Flower-tentacled Anglerfish.

These two fish were round as balls, with wide, gaping mouths and long, sharp, spine-like teeth. The usual stem rose from the snout, short, partly luminous, with a swollen, purple ball at the summit, which in turn, supported a pair of oval bodies. Around this bulb the encompassing white tissue burst into a circle of delicate fronds, flattened stems, branching into dozens of slender filaments, as lovely as an orchid, but doing what no orchid could ever do, giving forth light and flashes of light.

Each fish, as I have said, was spherical, as round as possible, with only the fins and tentacle to break the symmetry, except —and this exception was the unbelievable part—except for a second small fish which was grown fast to the lower surface of each of the larger ones, close in front of the median fin. Each Flower-tentacle, as I have said, possessed one of these living appendages, of exactly the same size and growing from the same spot. (Plate 33.)

Even a superficial examination showed that the larger fish belonged to one family (Linophrynidae), and the two dangling shreds to another (Aceratiidae). We should remember, however, that while we know this absorbing fact, the fish do not. We know our own scientific name is Homo sapiens, but I am tempted to perpetrate a ghastly pun and say that pragmatically the *iens* is too often elided, the remnant of the name holding good in the most slangy sense! A chimpanzee has no idea that we call him Anthropopithecus troglodytes, and Amoeba proteus has lived for untold millenniums, and will

284

32. *Blue-lighted Dragon Anglerfish.*

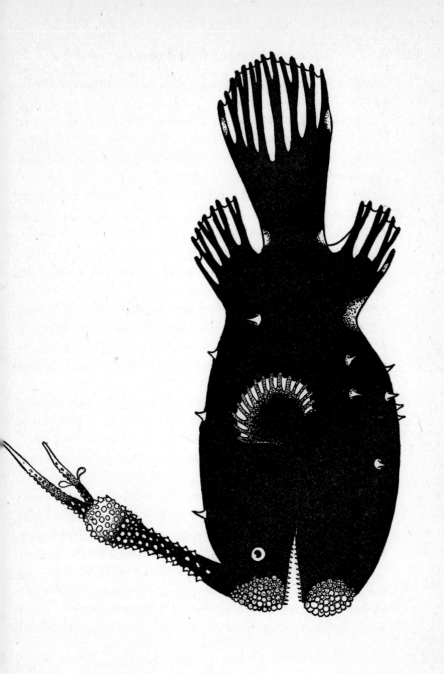

continue to do so, in happy ignorance of its binominal designation.

Occasionally, when our human-made taxonomic tree seems most firmly rooted and flourishing, a blight of a new discovery comes along and crashes an important branch. Of all birds in the world the English sparrow would seem to have had a settled perch on this evolutionary tree, and for centuries *Passer domesticus* has roosted peacefully among its fellow sparrows. Twelve short years ago, some over-curious ornithologist made it say "Ahhh!", looked into its beak, and saw there a most unsparrow-like arrangement of the palate, and instantly prescribed a short flight to the adjoining branch of weaverbirds, a wholly different family, Ploceidae. So if you are a vernacular purist, you must speak of the feathered pests around your house as Black-throated Weaverbirds. Only by such healthful pruning and grafting can our anthropomorphic science thrive, and approximate more and more the truth.

To return to our deep-sea anglers. We have here the unethical sight of a male fish of one family, grown fast to the female of a member of quite another of the First Families of Deep Ocean. One of these had to be given up, and in this particular case, according to the law of priority, the ladies retained their maiden name. The union is so remarkable that there is no simile or metaphor with which to introduce it. We know enough about this strange marriage in the black, icy abysses to be certain of the general outline of what occurs.

In the depths of the sea, both in the Atlantic and here in the Pacific, my nets have brought up hundreds of small sea devils, belonging, as we have believed, to some one of several families. They are always less than two inches in length, armed

286

33. *Flower-tentacled Mother Anglerfish.* The female fish is shown, natural size; its elaborate luminous tentacle, and the parasitic male fish.

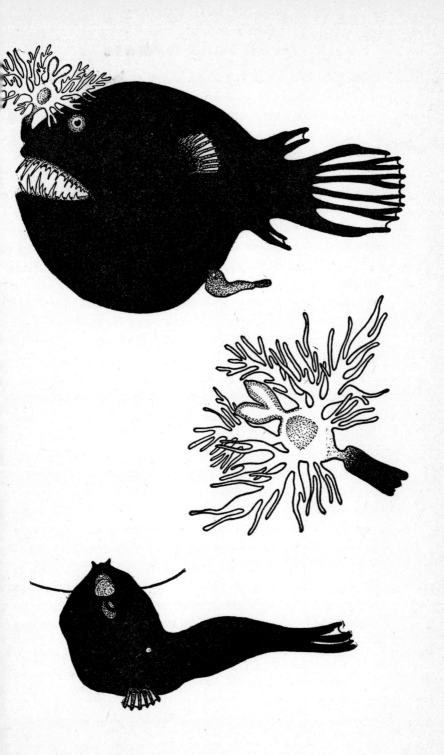

with no tentacle or lure, either fleshy or luminous, but with well-developed eyes, and relatively enormous nostrils, which sometimes occupy the entire front of the head. There is usually a projecting cluster of bristle-like teeth and small but efficient fins. Dissection has revealed no hint of ovaries or eggs among any of them, and almost all are immature, all but larvae.

This horde of dwarf males must be hatched in great numbers, how or where we do not know. But they swim through the cold, black depths of the sea, from a quarter to a full mile below the surface. In the course of time, one, perhaps out of thousands, scents a female and reaches her. She may be only relatively larger than he, as in the case of the Flower-tentacles which are only six or eight times as long. On the other hand, I have in my collection a female which is twenty times the length of the attached, parasitic male.

In external appearance these dwarfs seem to be normal fish, but they remain immature until their search is ended. These waste no time but rush at the object of their emotions, even two or three at once, and take firm hold wherever they chance to touch. This may, as in the present case, be on the side or the under part of the body, while others have been known to be satisfied with the front of the head, between the eyes. Their array of lip bristles enables the tiny fish to maintain a tight grip while, in some way, with their real teeth they chew directly through the skin. Like the gall on a plant induced by the sting of a minute wasp, the irritation of the gnawing male produces a low but distinct growth at the raw area. This soon unites with the capillaries in the mouth of the male, and a permanent, Siamese-twin attachment results. From now on he

288

is nourished by the flowing blood stream of the gargantuan female. The muscles of the male, his sense organs, brain, digestive tract, the very skeleton itself gradually disappear, and simultaneously he or it becomes adult. From now on, throughout all her life, the gentler sea-devil sex swims on her way with the tattered remains of her suitor dangling from her body.

Our anthropomorphic imagination can sympathize with a diminutive male spider climbing down the web of his prospective consort, gambling almost certain death against a moment of passion. At least he will have provided a lunch for his Brobdingnagian bride. But to be driven by impelling odour and light headlong upon a mate so gigantic, so impersonal, so unconscious of any emotion, in such Stygian darkness, and willfully to eat a hole in her tough hide, to feel the gradually increasing transfusion of her blood throughout one's veins, to lose everything that marked one as superior to a worm, to become a spineless, brainless, senseless thing that was a fish— this seems sheer fiction, absurd beyond all belief unless we have seen the proof of it.

This condition of a dwarf parasitic male combined with enforced physiological polyandry, would arouse only moderate astonishment in certain groups of backboneless animals. Our mind goes back to the paper nautilus, the squid-like male of which is extremely small, and which, in the process of matrimony, entrusts its mate with one of its living arms to treasure within her shell, for the purpose of fertilization when the eggs are laid.

But such happenings are unthinkable among the groups of vertebrates, unthinkable until we know that they do happen. Only in the mysterious depths of the ocean, still so little known, could such a phenomenon be conceivable, and on my desk here in our laboratory in the New York Zoological Park, the Flower-tentacles and their mates look out at me from their glass jars, still bound together, for better or for worse, literally flesh and blood of one another.

Did she know he was there? When did the last vestige of sight and smell, of heart-throb, of individual instinct and sensation, leave the little being? What theory or combination of theories of evolution can explain the gradual development through past ages, the *first* male to attach himself, culminating in this wholesale self-immolation on the altar of generation?

APPENDIX A

PUBLISHED SCIENTIFIC ARTICLES RELATING TO THE SECOND ZACA EXPEDITION

1. *Introduction, Itinerary, List of Stations, Nets and Dredges.* William Beebe. Zoologica, New York Zoological Society, 1938, Vol. XXIII, pp. 287-298.

2. *Seven New Marine Fishes from Lower California.* William Beebe and John Tee-Van. Zoologica, 1938, Vol. XXIII, pp. 299-312.

3. *Holothurians from the Western Coasts of Lower California and Central America, and from the Galapagos Islands.* Elisabeth Deichmann. Zoologica, 1938, Vol. XXIII, pp. 361-387.

4. *A Review of the American Fishes of the Family Cirrhitidae.* John Tee-Van. Zoologica, 1940, Vol. XXV, pp. 53-64.

5. *On the Post-embryonic Development of Brachyuran Crabs of the Genus Ocypode.* Jocelyn Crane. Zoologica, 1940, Vol. XXV, pp. 65-82.

6. *Actiniaria from the Gulf of California.* Oskar Carlgren. Zoologica, 1940, Vol. XXV, pp. 211-219.

7. *Medusae of the Templeton Crocker and Eastern Pacific Zaca Expeditions, 1936-1938.* Henry B. Bigelow. Zoologica, 1940, Vol. XXV, pp. 281-321.

8. *Notes on Enchinoderms from the West Coast of Central America.* Hubert Lyman Clark. Zoologica, 1940, Vol. XXV, pp. 331-352.

9. *Mollusks from the West Coast of Mexico and Central America. Part I.* Leo George Hertlein and A. M. Strong. Zoologica, 1940, Vol. XXV, pp. 369-430.

10. *External Characters of Six Embryo Nurse Sharks, Gin-*

glymostoma cirratum (*Gmelin*). William Beebe. Zoologica, 1941, Vol. XXVI, pp. 9-12.

11. *Polychaetous Annelids from the West Coast of Mexico and Central America.* Aaron L. Treadwell. Zoologica, 1941, Vol. XXVI, pp. 17-24.

12. *Fishes from the Tropical Eastern Pacific. Part I. Lancelets and Hag-Fishes.* William Beebe and John Tee-Van. Zoologica, 1941, Vol. XXVI, pp. 89-91.

13. *Fishes from the Tropical Eastern Pacific. Part II. Sharks.* William Beebe and John Tee-Van. Zoologica, 1941, Vol. XXVI, pp. 93-122.

14. *Crabs of the Genus Uca from the West Coast of Central America.* Jocelyn Crane. Zoologica, 1941, Vol. XXVI, pp. 145-208.

15. *A Study of Young Sailfish (Istiophorus).* William Beebe. Zoologica, 1941, Vol. XXVI, pp. 209-227.

16. *Fishes from the Tropical Eastern Pacific. Part III. Rays, Mantas and Chimaeras.* William Beebe and John Tee-Van. Zoologica, 1941, Vol. XXVI, pp. 245-280.

17. *On the Growth and Ecology of Brachyuran Crabs of the Genus Ocypode.* Jocelyn Crane. Zoologica, 1941, Vol. XXVI, pp. 297-310.

APPENDIX B

Text Identifications

APPENDIX B

APPENDIX B

APPENDIX B

APPENDIX B

297

APPENDIX B

INDEX

INDEX

INDEX

INDEX